POETRY
U. S. A.

EDITED BY PAUL MOLLOY

Cover Illustration: Katie McMurray
Scholastic Art Awards Winner

Interior Illustrations
Scholastic/Kodak Photography Awards Winners

SCHOLASTIC INC.
New York Toronto London Auckland Sydney

For reprint permission grateful acknowledgment is made to:

Appleton-Century-Crofts, an affiliate of Meredith Press, for "The Flower-Fed Buffaloes" from GOING TO THE STARS by Vachel Lindsay, copyright 1926 by D. Appleton & Co., copyright renewed 1954, by Elizabeth C. Lindsay.

Elizabeth Coatsworth Beston for "Concrete Trap" from POEMS, The Macmillan Company; originally appeared in *Saturday Review*.

Adrienne Rich Conrad for "Orient Wheat," copyright 1953 by Adrienne Rich Conrad; originally appeared in *The New Yorker*.

Curtis Brown Ltd. for "New Hampshire" and "The Poem" from A ROOF OF TIGER LILIES by Donald Hall, copyright © 1961 by Donald Hall. British Commonwealth rights to "Little Elegy" by X. J. Kennedy.

Andre Deutsch Limited for British Commonwealth rights to "New Hampshire" and "The Poem" by Donald Hall; "The Great Scarf of Birds" by John Updike.

Doubleday & Company, Inc., for "Little Elegy" from NUDE DESCENDING A STAIRCASE by X. J. Kennedy, copyright © 1960 by X. J. Kennedy, "Big Wind," copyright 1947 by The United Chapters of Phi Beta Kappa, "The Waking," copyright 1953 by Theodore Roethke, "My Papa's Waltz," copyright 1942 by Hearst Magazines, Inc., from COLLECTED POEMS OF THEODORE ROETHKE.

Norma Millay Ellis for "Eel-Grass," "Look Edwin," "Portrait by a Neighbor" by Edna St. Vincent Millay from COLLECTED POEMS, Harper & Row, copyright 1921, 1922, 1929, 1948, 1950, 1956 by Edna St. Vincent Millay and Norma Millay Ellis.

Faber and Faber Ltd. for British Commonwealth rights to "pity this busy monster manunkind" by E. E. Cummings; "Salem" by Robert Lowell; "I May, I Might, I Must" by Marianne Moore; "In a Station of the Metro" and "The River-Merchant's Wife" by Ezra Pound; "Silence" by Edwin Arlington Robinson; "The Emperor of Ice Cream" by Wallace Stevens; "Juggler" and "A Simile for Her Smile" by Richard Wilbur.

Robert Francis for "Aphrodite as History" and "While I Slept" from COME OUT INTO THE SUN, University Of Massachusetts Press, copyright by Robert Francis

Victor Gollancz Ltd. for British Commonwealth rights to "Ex-Basketball Player" by John Updike.

Grove Press, Inc., for "Permanently" from THANK YOU AND OTHER POEMS by Kenneth Koch, copyright © 1962 by Kenneth Koch.

Harcourt, Brace & World, Inc., for "pity this busy monster manunkind," copyright 1944 by E. E. Cummings, and "somewhere i have never travelled," copyright 1931, 1959 by E. E. Cummings, from POEMS 1923-1954 by E. E. Cummings; "Salem" from LORD WEARY'S CASTLE by Robert Lowell, copyright 1944, 1946 by Robert Lowell; "Juggler," copyright 1949 by Richard Wilbur, first appeared in *The New Yorker*, and "A Simile for Her Smile," copyright 1948, 1949, 1950 by Richard Wilbur, from CEREMONY AND OTHER POEMS.

Harper & Row, Publishers, Incorporated, for "Piano After War" from SELECTED POEMS by Gwendolyn Brooks, copyright 1945 by Gwendolyn Brooks Blakely; "Traveling Through the Dark" from TRAVELING THROUGH THE DARK AND OTHER POEMS by William Stafford, copyright © 1960 by William Stafford;

The Viking Press, Inc., for "First Lesson" from LETTER FROM A DISTANT LAND by Philip Booth, copyright © 1957 by Philip Booth; "Midcentury Love Letter" from TIMES THREE by Phyllis McGinley, copyright 1953 by Phyllis McGinley, originally appeared in *The New Yorker;* "I May, I Might. I Must" from O TO BE A DRAGON by Marianne Moore.

Wesleyan University Press for "Cat on a Couch" from LIGHT AND DARK by Barbara Howes, copyright © 1955 by Barbara Howes.

Photo Credits

Page 14 by David Pfeil, Alamo Heights H.S., San Antonio, Texas ● page 30 by Stephen Hawley, Boulder (Colo.) H.S. ● page 42 by Sandra Maddalena, Central Jr. H.S., Quincy, Mass. ● page 64 by Neil Baumgarten, Baltimore (Md.) Polytechnic Institute ● page 78 by Ernest Link, Reidsville (N.C.) H.S. ● page 90 by Jeff Douglas, Santa Monica (Calif.) H.S. ● page 106 by Dennis Pierce, Santa Monica (Calif.) H.S.

Cover Design by Marijka Kostiw

ISBN 0-590-35586-4

12 11 10 9   9/9 0/0

Printed in the U.S.A.   40

CONTENTS

PEOPLE, GROUP ONE

ALIVE AND SPOKEN, GROUP TWO

9

POEMS OF THE CITY, GROUP FIVE

THE GOOD WILDERNESS, GROUP SIX

MORE FIGURATIVELY, GROUP SEVEN

FARTHER OUT, GROUP EIGHT

ACKNOWLEDGMENTS

For criticism, encouragement, and good counsel, I am grateful to my wife Anne; to my students and colleagues at Phillips Exeter, especially Richard Niebling and William Bates; to my friends and editors at Scholastic, especially Richard Robinson and Lynn McMillen; to Thomas Folds of the Metropolitan Museum of Art; to Hyde Cox; and to the poets Elizabeth Coatsworth, Robert Fitzgerald, Robert Francis, Donald Hall, X. J. Kennedy, Denise Levertov, Adrienne Rich, Louis Simpson, W. J. Snodgrass, Gary Snyder, May Swenson, and Richard Wilbur.

P.M.

A WORD TO STUDENTS

This anthology has been designed for your reading pleasure. Each poem, therefore, is presented without the interference of numbers and symbols necessary to designate footnotes. If you have difficulty with any words or terms in a particular poem, consult the "Note" on that poem at the back of this book. These "Notes," beginning on page 126 contain the definitions of words and terms that other students have found troublesome and also some words of explanation about the poems by the poets themselves.

FOREWORD

Poetry U.S.A. is intended for students in their middle high school years. To insure the practicality of the selections, I have tried each poem with students in my ninth, tenth, and eleventh grade classes. All of the poems that appear in this anthology have met the test of my students' interest and enthusiasm.

This poetry collection has two basic aims. The first is to give students an idea of the rich variety and appeal of American poetry. Fifty-five American poets are represented, ranging from the nineteenth century poets Whitman and Thoreau to the contemporary poets Roethke and Wilbur. For ease of reading and discussion, the one hundred five poems in the anthology are grouped under eight headings. Some of these groupings are based on themes and some concentrate on particular techniques of poetry.

The second aim of the anthology is to introduce students to rhetorical devices used in poetry, with special attention to the use of figurative language. Many of the poems, particularly those in the group "More Figuratively," have been selected for their richness of metaphor. Because, in its broadest sense, poetry *is* metaphor, it is important for students to recognize this device and to understand how it operates. Robert Frost once said, "Education by poetry is education by metaphor. . . . Poetry begins in trivial metaphors, pretty metaphors, 'grace' metaphors, and goes on to the profoundest thinking that we have." It is hoped that the poems in this anthology will help students find their way to the profundities of which Frost spoke.

PAUL MOLLOY

Phillips Exeter Academy
Exeter, New Hampshire

PEOPLE

LIGHTHEARTED WILLIAM
William Carlos Williams

Lighthearted William twirled
his November moustaches
and, half dressed, looked
from the bedroom window
upon the spring weather.

Heigh-ya! sighed he gaily
leaning out to see
up and down the street
where a heavy sunlight
lay beyond some blue shadows.

Into the room he drew
his head again and laughed
to himself quietly
twirling his green moustaches.

THE GUM-GATHERER
Robert Frost

There overtook me and drew me in
To his down-hill, early-morning stride,
And set me five miles on my road
Better than if he had had me ride,
A man with a swinging bag for load
And half the bag wound round his hand.
We talked like barking above the din
Of water we walked along beside.
And for my telling him where I'd been
And where I lived in mountain land
To be coming home the way I was,
He told me a little about himself.
He came from higher up in the pass
Where the grist of the new-beginning brooks
Is blocks split off the mountain mass—
And hopeless grist enough it looks
Ever to grind to soil for grass.
(The way it is will do for moss.)
There he had built his stolen shack.
It had to be a stolen shack

Because of the fears of fire and loss
That trouble the sleep of lumber folk:
Visions of half the world burned black
And the sun shrunken yellow in smoke.
We know who when they come to town
Bring berries under the wagon seat,
Or a basket of eggs between their feet;
What this man brought in a cotton sack
Was gum, the gum of the mountain spruce.
He showed me lumps of the scented stuff
Like uncut jewels, dull and rough.
It comes to market golden brown;
But turns to pink between the teeth.

I told him this is a pleasant life
To set your breast to the bark of trees
That all your days are dim beneath,
And reaching up with a little knife,
To loose the resin and take it down
And bring it to market when you please.

MY PAPA'S WALTZ
Theodore Roethke

The whisky on your breath
Could make a small boy dizzy;
But I hung on like death:
Such waltzing was not easy.

We romped until the pan
Slid from the kitchen shelf;
My mother's countenance
Could not unfrown itself.

The hand that held my wrist
Was battered on one knuckle;
At every step you missed
My right ear scraped a buckle.

You beat time on my head
With a palm caked hard by dirt,
Then waltzed me off to bed
Still clinging to your shirt.

THE CENTAUR
May Swenson

The summer that I was ten —
Can it be there was only one
summer that I was ten? It must

have been a long one then —
each day I'd go out to choose
a fresh horse from my stable

which was a willow grove
down by the old canal.
I'd go on my two bare feet

But when, with my brother's jack-knife,
I had cut me a long limber horse
with a good thick knob for a head,

and peeled him slick and clean
except a few leaves for the tail,
and cinched my brother's belt

around his head for a rein,
I'd straddle and canter him fast
up the grass bank to the path,

trot along in the lovely dust
that talcumed over his hoofs,
hiding my toes, and turning

his feet to swift half-moons.
The willow knob with the strap
jouncing between my thighs

was the pommel and yet the poll
of my nickering pony's head.
My head and my neck were mine,

yet they were shaped like a horse.
My hair flopped to the side
like the mane of a horse in the wind.

My forelock swung in my eyes,
my neck arched and I snorted.
I shied and skittered and reared,

stopped and raised my knees,
pawed at the ground and quivered.
My teeth bared as we wheeled

and swished through the dust again.
I was the horse and the rider,
and the leather I slapped to his rump

spanked on my own behind.
Doubled, my two hoofs beat
a gallop along the bank,

the wind twanged in my mane,
my mouth squared to the bit.
And yet I sat on my steed

quiet, negligent riding,
my toes standing the stirrups,
my thighs hugging his ribs.

At a walk we drew up to the porch.
I tethered him to a paling.
Dismounting, I smoothed my skirt

and entered the dusky hall.
My feet on the clean linoleum
left ghostly toes in the hall.

Where have you been? said my mother.
Been riding, I said from the sink,
and filled me a glass of water.

What's that in your pocket? she said.
Just my knife. It weighted my pocket
and stretched my dress awry.

Go tie back your hair, said my mother,
and *Why is your mouth all green?*
*Rob Roy, he pulled some clover
as we crossed the field*, I told her.

PORTRAIT BY A NEIGHBOR
Edna St. Vincent Millay

Before she has her floor swept
  Or her dishes done,
Any day you'll find her
  A-sunning in the sun!

It's long after midnight
  Her key's in the lock,
And you never see her chimney smoke
  Till past ten o'clock!

She digs in her garden
  With a shovel and a spoon,
She weeds her lazy lettuce
  By the light of the moon.

She walks up the walk
  Like a woman in a dream,
She forgets she borrowed butter
  And pays you back cream!

Her lawn looks like a meadow,
  And if she mows the place
She leaves the clover standing
  And the Queen Anne's lace!

MINIVER CHEEVY

Edwin Arlington Robinson

Miniver Cheevy, child of scorn,
   Grew lean while he assailed the seasons;
He wept that he was ever born,
   And he had reasons.

Miniver loved the days of old
   When swords were bright and steeds were prancing.
The vision of a warrior bold
   Would set him dancing.

Miniver sighed for what was not,
   And dreamed, and rested from his labors;
He dreamed of Thebes and Camelot,
   And Priam's neighbors.

Miniver mourned the ripe renown
   That made so many a name so fragrant;
He mourned Romance, now on the town,
   And Art, a vagrant.

Miniver loved the Medici,
   Albeit he had never seen one;
He would have sinned incessantly
   Could he have been one.

Miniver cursed the commonplace
   And eyed a khaki suit with loathing;
He missed the medieval grace
   Of iron clothing.

Miniver scorned the gold he sought,
   But sore annoyed was he without it;
Miniver thought, and thought, and thought,
   And thought about it.

Miniver Cheevy, born too late,
   Scratched his head and kept on thinking:
Miniver coughed, and called it fate,
   And kept on drinking.

GEORGE GRAY
Edgar Lee Masters

I have studied many times
The marble which was chiseled for me —
A boat with a furled sail at rest in a harbor.
In truth it pictures not my destination
But my life.
For love was offered me and I shrank from its
   disillusionment;
Sorrow knocked at my door, but I was afraid;
Ambition called to me, but I dreaded the chances.
Yet all the while I hungered for meaning in my life.
And now I know that we must lift the sail
And catch the winds of destiny
Wherever they drive the boat.
To put meaning in one's life may end in madness,
But life without meaning is the torture
Of restlessness and vague desire —
It is a boat longing for the sea and yet afraid.

LUCINDA MATLOCK
Edgar Lee Masters

I went to the dances at Chandlerville,
And played snap-out at Winchester,
One time we changed partners,
Driving home in the moonlight of middle June,
And then I found Davis.
We were married and lived together for seventy years,
Enjoying, working, raising the twelve children,
Eight of whom we lost
Ere I had reached the age of sixty.
I spun, I wove, I kept the house, I nursed the sick,
I made the garden, and for holiday
Rambled over the fields where sang the larks,
And by Spoon River gathering many a shell,
And many a flower and medicinal weed—
Shouting to the wooded hills, singing to the green valleys.
At ninety-six I had lived enough, that is all,
And passed to a sweet repose.
What is this I hear of sorrow and weariness,
Anger, discontent and drooping hopes?
Degenerate sons and daughters,
Life is too strong for you—
It takes life to love Life.

WILLIAM GOODE
Edgar Lee Masters

To all in the village I seemed, no doubt,
To go this way and that way, aimlessly.
But here by the river you can see at twilight
The soft-winged bats fly zig-zag here and there —
They must fly so to catch their food.
And if you have ever lost your way at night,
In the deep wood near Miller's Ford,
And dodged this way and now that,
Wherever the light of the Milky Way shone through,
Trying to find the path,
You should understand I sought the way
With earnest zeal, and all my wanderings
Were wanderings in the quest.

FIDDLER JONES
Edgar Lee Masters

The earth keeps some vibration going
There in your heart, and that is you.
And if the people find you can fiddle,
Why, fiddle you must, for all your life.
What do you see, a harvest of clover?
Or a meadow to walk through to the river?
The wind's in the corn; you rub your hands
For beeves hereafter ready for market;
Or else you hear the rustle of skirts
Like the girls when dancing at Little Grove.
To Cooney Potter a pillar of dust
Or whirling leaves meant ruinous drouth;
They looked to me like Red-Head Sammy
Stepping it off, to "Toor-a-Loor."
How could I till my forty acres
Not to speak of getting more,
With a medley of horns, bassoons and piccolos
Stirred in my brain by crows and robins
And the creak of a wind-mill—only these?
And I never started to plow in my life
That some one did not stop in the road
And take me away to a dance or picnic.
I ended up with forty acres;
I ended up with a broken fiddle—
And a broken laugh, and a thousand memories,
And not a single regret.

EX-BASKETBALL PLAYER

John Updike

Pearl Avenue runs past the high school lot,
Bends with the trolley tracks, and stops, cut off
Before it has a chance to go two blocks,
At Colonel McComsky Plaza. Berth's Garage
Is on the corner facing west, and there,
Most days, you'll find Flick Webb, who helps Berth out.

Flick stands tall among the idiot pumps—
Five on a side, the old bubble-head style,
Their rubber elbows hanging loose and low.
One's nostrils are two S's, and his eyes
An E and O. And one is squat, without
A head at all—more of a football type.

Once, Flick played for the high school team, the Wizards.
He was good: in fact, the best. In '46,
He bucketed three hundred ninety points,
A county record still. The ball loved Flick.
I saw him rack up thirty-eight or forty
In one home game. His hands were like wild birds.

He never learned a trade; he just sells gas,
Checks oil, and changes flats. Once in a while,
As a gag, he dribbles an inner tube,
But most of us remember anyway.
His hands are fine and nervous on the lug wrench.
It makes no difference to the lug wrench, though.

Off work, he hangs around Mae's Luncheonette.
Grease-grey and kind of coiled, he plays pinball,
Sips lemon Cokes, and smokes those thin cigars;
Flick seldom speaks to Mae, just sits and nods
Beyond her face towards bright applauding tiers
Of Necco Wafers, Nibs, and Juju Beads.

KING JUKE
Kenneth Fearing

The jukebox has a big square face,
A majestic face, softly glowing with red and green and purple
　lights.
Have you got a face as bright as that?

BUT IT'S A PROVEN FACT THAT A JUKEBOX HAS
　NO EARS.

With its throat of brass, the jukebox eats live nickels raw;
It can turn itself on or shut itself off;
It has no hangovers, knows no regrets, and it never feels the
　need for sleep.
Can you do that?
What can you do that a jukebox can't, and do it ten times
　better than you?

And it hammers at your nerves, and stabs you through the
　heart, and beats upon your soul—
But can you do that to the box?

Its resourceful mind, filled with thoughts that range from
　love to grief, from the gutter to the stars, from pole to pole,
Can seize its thoughts between fingers of steel,
Begin them at the start and follow them through in an orderly
　fashion to the very end.
Can you do that?
And what can you say that a jukebox can't, and say it in a
　clearer, louder voice than yours?
What have you got, a jukebox hasn't got?

Well, a jukebox has no ears, they say.
The box, it is believed, cannot even hear itself.
IT SIMPLY HAS NO EARS AT ALL.

ALIVE AND
SPOKEN

APHRODITE AS HISTORY
Robert Francis

Though the marble is ancient
It is only an ancient
Copy and though the lost
Original was still more ancient
Still it was not Praxiteles
Only a follower of Praxiteles
And Praxiteles was not the first.

I'M NOBODY! WHO ARE YOU?
Emily Dickinson

I'm nobody! Who are you?
Are you nobody, too?
Then there's a pair of us—don't tell!
They'd banish us, you know.

How dreary to be somebody!
How public, like a frog
To tell your name the livelong day
To an admiring bog!

THIS IS JUST TO SAY
William Carlos Williams

I have eaten
the plums
that were in
the icebox

and which
you were probably
saving
for breakfast

Forgive me
they were delicious
so sweet
and so cold

LOOK, EDWIN!
Edna St. Vincent Millay

Look, Edwin! Do you see that boy
Talking to that other boy?
No, over there by those two men —
Wait, don't look now — now look again.
No, not the one in navy-blue;
That's the one he's talking to.
Sure you see him? Striped pants?
Well, *he was born in Paris, France*.

REASON
Josephine Miles

Said, Pull her up a bit will you, Mac, I want to unload there.
Said, Pull her up my rear end, first come first serve.
Said, Give her the gun, Bud, he needs a taste of his own
    bumper.
Then the usher came and got into the act:

Said, Pull her up, pull her up a bit, we need this space, sir.
Said, For God's sake, is this still a free country or what,
You go back and take care of Gary Cooper's horse
And leave me handle my own car.

Saw them unloading the lame old lady,
Ducked out under the wheel and gave her an elbow,
Said, All you needed to do was just explain;
Reason, Reason is my middle name.

I TASTE A LIQUOR NEVER BREWED
Emily Dickinson

I taste a liquor never brewed,
From tankards scooped in pearl;
Not all the vats upon the Rhine
Yield such an alcohol!

Inebriate of air am I,
And debauchee of dew,
Reeling, through endless summer days,
From inns of molten blue.

When landlords turn the drunken bee
Out of the foxglove's door,
When butterflies renounce their drams,
I shall but drink the more!

Till seraphs swing their snowy hats,
And saints to windows run,
To see the little tippler
Leaning against the sun!

THE PEDIGREE OF HONEY
Emily Dickinson

The pedigree of honey
Does not concern the bee;
A clover, any time, to him
Is aristocracy.

SILENCE
Marianne Moore

My father used to say,
"Superior people never make long visits,
have to be shown Longfellow's grave
or the glass flowers at Harvard.
Self-reliant like the cat —
that takes its prey to privacy,
the mouse's limp tail hanging like a shoelace from its mouth —
they sometimes enjoy solitude,
and can be robbed of speech
by speech that has delighted them.
The deepest feeling always shows itself in silence;
not in silence, but restraint."
Nor was he insincere in saying, "Make my house your inn."
Inns are not residences.

I MAY, I MIGHT, I MUST
Marianne Moore

If you will tell me why the fen
appears impassable, I then
will tell you why I think that I
can get across it if I try.

COBB WOULD HAVE CAUGHT IT

Robert Fitzgerald

In sunburnt parks where Sundays lie,
Or the wide wastes beyond the cities,
Teams in grey deploy through sunlight.

Talk it up, boys, a little practice.

Coming in stubby and fast, the baseman
Gathers a grounder in fat green grass,
Picks it stinging and clipped as wit
Into the leather: a swinging step
Wings it deadeye down to first.
Smack. Oh, attaboy, attyoldboy.

Catcher reverses his cap, pulls down
Sweaty casque, and squats in the dust:
Pitcher rubs new ball on his pants,
Chewing, puts a jet behind him;
Nods past batter, taking his time.
Batter settles, tugs at his cap:
A spinning ball: step and swing to it,
Caught like a cheek before it ducks
By shivery hickory: socko, baby:
Cleats dig into dust. Outfielder,
On his way, looking over shoulder,
Makes it a triple. A long peg home.

Innings and afternoons. Fly lost in sunset.
Throwing arm gone bad. There's your old ball game.
Cool reek of the field. Reek of companions.

HAY FOR THE HORSES
Gary Snyder

He had driven half the night
From far down San Joaquin
Through Mariposa, up the
Dangerous mountain roads,
And pulled in at eight a.m.
With his big truckload of hay behind the barn.
With winch and ropes and hooks
We stacked the bales up clean
To splintery redwood rafters
High in the dark, flecks of alfalfa
Whirling through shingle-cracks of light,
Itch of haydust in the sweaty shirt and shoes.
At lunchtime under Black oak
Out in the hot corral,
— The old mare nosing lunchpails,
Grasshoppers crackling in the weeds —
"I'm sixty-eight," he said,
"I first bucked hay when I was seventeen.
I thought, that day I started,
I sure would hate to do this all my life.
And dammit, that's just what
I've gone and done."

THE MOST OF IT
Robert Frost

He thought he kept the universe alone;
For all the voice in answer he could wake
Was but the mocking echo of his own
From some tree-hidden cliff across the lake.
Some morning from the boulder-broken beach
He would cry out on life, that what it wants
Is not its own love back in copy speech,
But counter-love, original response.
And nothing ever came of what he cried
Unless it was the embodiment that crashed
In the cliff's talus on the other side,
And then in the far distant water splashed,
But after a time allowed for it to swim,
Instead of proving human when it neared
And someone else additional to him,
As a great buck it powerfully appeared,
Pushing the crumpled water up ahead,
And landed pouring like a waterfall,
And stumbled through the rocks with horny tread,
And forced the underbrush—and that was all.

PITY THIS BUSY MONSTER MANUNKIND
E. E. Cummings

pity this busy monster, manunkind,

not. Progress is a comfortable disease:
your victim (death and life safely beyond)

plays with the bigness of his littleness
—electrons deify one razorblade
into a mountainrange; lenses extend

unwish through curving wherewhen till unwish
returns on its unself.

                A world of made
is not a world of born—pity poor flesh

and trees, poor stars and stones, but never this
fine specimen of hypermagical

ultraomnipotence. We doctors know

a hopeless case if—listen: there's a hell
of a good universe next door; let's go

THE EMPEROR OF ICE CREAM
Wallace Stevens

Call the roller of big cigars,
The muscular one, and bid him whip
In kitchen cups concupiscent curds.
Let the wenches dawdle in such dress
As they are used to wear, and let the boys
Bring flowers in last month's newspapers.
Let be be finale of seem.
The only emperor is the emperor of ice cream.

Take from the dresser of deal,
Lacking the three glass knobs, that sheet
On which she embroidered fantails once
And spread it so as to cover her face.
If her horny feet protrude, they come
To show how cold she is, and dumb.
Let the lamp affix its beam.
The only emperor is the emperor of ice cream.

LOVE POEMS

LOVE SONG
John R. Nash

This, that I carry like a butterfly,
prisoner in my cupped and outstretched hands,
is, of all things, small,
but great in its demands
and bears within itself a world of power.
I close my hand upon it like a wall.
For this there can be neither time nor season
and of all things upon the earth
it has the least to do with reason.
(I open my hand, finger from palm. Look!)
This holds within it life, death, and birth;
used wrong, there is no harm it cannot do.
Look long, look carefully;
this is for you.

A DECADE
Amy Lowell

When you came, you were like red wine and honey,
And the taste of you burnt my mouth with its sweetness.
Now you are like morning bread,
Smooth and pleasant.
I hardly taste you at all for I know your savor,
But I am completely nourished.

A SIMILE FOR HER SMILE
Richard Wilbur

Your smiling, or the hope, the thought of it,
Makes in my mind such pause and abrupt ease
As when the highway bridgegates fall,
Balking the hasty traffic, which must sit
On each side massed and staring, while
Deliberately the drawbridge starts to rise:

Then horns are hushed, the oilsmoke rarefies,
Above the idling motors one can tell
The packet's smooth approach, the slip,
Slip of the silken river past the sides,
The ringing of clear bells, the dip
And slow cascading of the paddle wheel.

MIDCENTURY LOVE LETTER
Phyllis McGinley

Stay near me. Speak my name. Oh, do not wander
By a thought's span, heart's impulse, from the light
We kindle here. You are my sole defender
(As I am yours) in this precipitous night,
Which over earth, till common landmarks alter,
Is falling, without stars, and bitter cold.
We two have but our burning selves for shelter.
Huddle against me. Give me your hand to hold.

So might two climbers lost in mountain weather
On a high slope and taken by the storm,
Desperate in the darkness, cling together
Under one cloak and breathe each other warm.
Stay near me. Spirit, perishable as bone,
In no such winter can survive alone.

PERMANENTLY
Kenneth Koch

One day the Nouns were clustered in the street.
An Adjective walked by, with her dark beauty.
The Nouns were struck, moved, changed.
The next day a Verb drove up, and created the Sentence.

Each Sentence says one thing—for example, "Although it was
   a dark rainy day when the Adjective walked by, I shall
   remember the pure and sweet expression on her face until
   the day I perish from the green, effective earth."
Or, "Will you please close the window, Andrew?"
Or, for example, "Thank you, the pink pot of flowers on the
   window sill has changed color recently to a light yellow,
   due to the heat from the boiler factory which exists
   nearby."

In the springtime the Sentences and the Nouns lay silently on
   the grass.
A lonely Conjunction here and there would call, "And! But!"
But the Adjective did not emerge.

As the adjective is lost in the sentence,
So I am lost in your eyes, ears, nose, and throat—
You have enchanted me with a single kiss
Which can never be undone
Until the destruction of language.

COOL TOMBS
Carl Sandburg

When Abraham Lincoln was shoveled into the tombs, he
forgot the copperheads and the assassin . . . in the dust,
in the cool tombs.

And Ulysses Grant lost all thought of con men and Wall
Street, cash and collateral turned ashes . . . in the
dust, in the cool tombs.

Pocahontas's body, lovely as a poplar, sweet as a red haw in
November or a pawpaw in May, did she wonder? does
she remember? . . . in the dust, in the cool tombs?

Take any streetful of people buying clothes and groceries,
cheering a hero or throwing confetti and blowing tin
horns . . . tell me if the lovers are losers . . . tell me if
any get more than the lovers . . . in the dust . . . in
the cool tombs.

ANNE RUTLEDGE

Edgar Lee Masters

Out of me unworthy and unknown
The vibrations of deathless music;
"With malice toward none, with charity for all."
Out of me the forgiveness of millions toward millions,
And the beneficent face of a nation
Shining with justice and truth.
I am Anne Rutledge who sleep beneath these weeds,
Beloved in life of Abraham Lincoln,
Wedded to him, not through union,
But through separation.
Bloom forever, O Republic,
From the dust of my bosom!

THE FIRE OF DRIFT-WOOD
Devereaux Farm, Near Marblehead
Henry Wadsworth Longfellow

We sat within the farm-house old,
 Whose windows, looking o'er the bay,
Gave to the sea-breeze damp and cold
 An easy entrance, night and day.

Not far away we saw the port,
 The strange, old-fashioned, silent town,
The lighthouse, the dismantled fort,
 The wooden houses, quaint and brown.

We sat and talked until the night,
 Descending, filled the little room;
Our faces faded from the sight,
 Our voices only broke the gloom.

We spake of many a vanished scene,
 Of what we once had thought and said,
Of what had been, and might have been,
 And who was changed, and who was dead;

And all that fills the hearts of friends,
 When first they feel, with secret pain,
Their lives thenceforth have separate ends,
 And never can be one again;

The first slight swerving of the heart,
 That words are powerless to express,
And leave it still unsaid in part,
 Or say it in too great excess.

The very tones in which we spake
   Had something strange, I could but mark;
The leaves of memory seemed to make
   A mournful rustling in the dark.

Oft died the words upon our lips,
   As suddenly, from out the fire
Built of the wreck of stranded ships,
   The flames would leap and then expire.

And, as their splendor flashed and failed,
   We thought of wrecks upon the main,
Of ships dismasted, that were hailed
   And sent no answer back again.

The windows, rattling in their frames,
   The ocean, roaring up the beach,
The gusty blast, the bickering flames,
   All mingled vaguely in our speech;

Until they made themselves a part
   Of fancies floating through the brain,
The long-lost ventures of the heart,
   That send no answers back again.

O flames that glowed! O hearts that yearned!
   They were indeed too much akin,
The drift-wood fire without that burned,
   The thoughts that burned and glowed within.

WHILE I SLEPT
Robert Francis

While I slept, while I slept and the night grew colder
She would come to my bedroom stepping softly
And draw a blanket about my shoulder
While I slept.

While I slept, while I slept in the dark still heat
She would come to my bedside stepping coolly
And smooth the twisted troubled sheet
While I slept.

Now she sleeps, sleeps under quiet rain
While nights grow warm or nights grow colder
And I wake and sleep and wake again
While she sleeps.

THE RIVER-MERCHANT'S WIFE: A LETTER
(From the Chinese of Li Po)
Ezra Pound, translator

While my hair was still cut straight across my forehead
I played about the front gate, pulling flowers.
You came by on bamboo stilts, playing horse;
You walked about my seat, playing with blue plums.
And we went on living in the village of Chokan:
Two small people, without dislike or suspicion.

At fourteen I married My Lord you.
I never laughed, being bashful.
Lowering my head, I looked at the wall.
Called to, a thousand times, I never looked back.

At fifteen I stopped scowling,
I desired my dust to be mingled with yours
Forever and forever, and forever.
Why should I climb the look-out?

At sixteen you departed,
You went into far Ku-to-Yen, by the river of swirling eddies,
And you have been gone five months.
The monkeys make sorrowful noise overhead.
You dragged your feet when you went out.
By the gate now, the moss is grown, the different mosses,
Too deep to clear them away!
The leaves fall early this autumn, in wind.
The paired butterflies are already yellow with August
Over the grass in the west garden—
They hurt me.
I grow older.
If you are coming down through the narrows of the river,
Please let me know beforehand,
And I will come out to meet you,
    As far as Cho-fu-Sa.

DVONYA
Louis Simpson

In the town of Odessa
There is a garden
And Dvonya is there . . .
Dvonya, whom I love
Though I have never been in Odessa.

I love her black hair, and eyes
As green as a salad
That you gather in the woods in August
Between the roots of alder,
Her skin, with an odor of wildflowers.

We understand each other perfectly.
We are cousins twice removed.
In the garden we drink our tea,
Discussing the plays of Chekhov
As evening falls and the lights begin to twinkle.

But this is only a dream.
I am not there with my thin hands
And citified speech,
And the old woman is not there
Peering between the curtains.

We are only phantoms, bits of ash,
Like yesterday's newspaper
Or the smoke of chimneys.
All that passed long ago
On a summer night in Odessa.

SOMEWHERE I HAVE NEVER TRAVELLED
E. E. Cummings

somewhere i have never travelled, gladly beyond
any experience, your eyes have their silence:
in your most frail gesture are things which enclose me,
or which i cannot touch because they are too near

your slightest look easily will unclose me
though i have closed myself as fingers,
you open always petal by petal myself as Spring opens
(touching skilfully, mysteriously) her first rose

or if your wish be to close me, i and
my life will shut very beautifully, suddenly,
as when the heart of this flower imagines
the snow carefully everywhere descending;

nothing which we are to perceive in this world equals
the power of your intense fragility: whose texture
compels me with the colour of its countries,
rendering death and forever with each breathing

(i do not know what it is about you that closes
and opens; only something in me understands
the voice of your eyes is deeper than all roses)
nobody, not even the rain, has such small hands

WAR POEMS

CAVALRY CROSSING A FORD
Walt Whitman

A line in long array where they wind betwixt green islands,
They take a serpentine course, their arms flash in the sun —
   hark to the musical clank,
Behold the silvery river, in it the splashing horses loitering
   stop to drink,
Behold the brown-faced men, each group, each person a pic-
   ture, the negligent rest on the saddles,
Some emerge on the opposite bank, others are just entering
   the ford — while,
Scarlet and blue and snowy white,
The guidon flags flutter gayly in the wind.

VOLUNTARIES
Ralph Waldo Emerson

In an age of fops and toys,
Wanting wisdom, void of right,
Who shall nerve heroic boys
To hazard all in Freedom's fight —
Break sharply off their jolly games,
Forsake their comrades gay
And quit proud homes and youthful dames
For famine, toil, and fray?
Yet on the nimble air benign
Speed nimbler messages,
That waft the breath of grace divine
To hearts in sloth and ease.
So nigh is grandeur to our dust,
So near is God to man,
When Duty whispers low, *Thou must*,
The youth replies, *I can*.

I HAVE A RENDEZVOUS WITH DEATH
Alan Seeger

I have a rendezvous with Death
At some disputed barricade,
When spring comes back with rustling shade
And apple-blossoms fill the air.
I have a rendezvous with Death
When spring brings back blue days and fair.

It may be he shall take my hand
And lead me into his dark land
And close my eyes and quench my breath.
It may be I shall pass him still.
I have a rendezvous with Death
On some scarred slope of battered hill
When spring comes round again this year
And the first meadow flowers appear.

God knows 'twere better to be deep
Pillowed in silk and scented down,
Where love throbs out in blissful sleep,
Pulse nigh to pulse, and breath to breath,
Where hushed awakenings are dear . . .
But I've a rendezvous with Death
At midnight in some flaming town,
When Spring trips north again this year,
And I to my pledged word am true,
I shall not fail that rendezvous.

WAR IS KIND

Stephen Crane

Do not weep, maiden, for war is kind.
Because your lover threw wild hands toward the sky
And the affrighted steed ran on alone,
Do not weep.
War is kind.

    Hoarse, booming drums of the regiment,
    Little souls who thirst for fight,
    These men were born to drill and die.
    The unexplained glory flies above them,
    Great is the battle god, great, and his kingdom
    A field where a thousand corpses lie.

Do not weep, babe, for war is kind.
Because your father tumbled in the yellow trenches,
Raged at his breast, gulped and died,
Do not weep.
War is kind.

    Swift blazing flag of the regiment,
    Eagle with crest of red and gold,
    These men were born to drill and die.
    Point for them the virtue of slaughter,
    Make plain to them the excellence of killing
    And a field where a thousand corpses lie.

Mother whose heart hung humble as a button
On the bright splendid shroud of your son,
Do not weep.
War is kind.

THE ASH AND THE OAK
Louis Simpson

When men discovered freedom first
The fighting was on foot,
They were encouraged by their thirst
And promises of loot,
And when it feathered and bows boomed
Their virtue was a root.

O the ash and the oak and the willow tree
And green grows the grass on the infantry!

At Malplaquet and Waterloo
They were polite and proud,
They primed their guns with billets-doux
And, as they fired, bowed.
At Appomattox too, it seems
Some things were understood.

O the ash and the oak and the willow tree
And green grows the grass on the infantry!

But at Verdun and at Bastogne
There was a great recoil,
The blood was bitter to the bone
The trigger to the soul,
And death was nothing if not dull,
A hero was a fool.

O the ash and the oak and the willow tree
And that's an end of the infantry.

SUCCESS IS COUNTED SWEETEST

Emily Dickinson

Success is counted sweetest
By those who ne'er succeed.
To comprehend a nectar
Requires sorest need.

Not one of all the purple host
Who took the flag today
Can tell the definition,
So clear, of victory,

As he, defeated, dying,
On whose forbidden ear
The distant strains of triumph
Burst, agonized and clear.

PIANO AFTER WAR

Gwendolyn Brooks

On a snug evening I shall watch her fingers,
Cleverly ringed, declining to clever pink,
Beg glory from the willing keys. Old hungers
Will break their coffins, rise to eat and thank.
And music, warily, like the golden rose
That sometimes after sunset warms the west,
Will warm that room persuasively suffuse
That room and me, rejuvenate a past.
But suddenly, across my climbing fever
Of proud delight—a multiplying cry.
A cry of bitter dead men who will never
Attend a gentle maker of musical joy.
Then my thawed eye will go again to ice,
And stone will shove the softness from my face.

EIGHTH AIR FORCE
Randall Jarrell

If, in an odd angle of the hutment
A puppy laps the water from a can
Of flowers, and the drunk sergeant shaving
Whistles *O Paradiso!* — shall I say that man
Is not as men have said: a wolf to man?

The other murderers troop in yawning;
Three of them play Pitch, one sleeps, and one
Lies counting missions, lies there sweating
Till even his heart beats: One; One; One.
O murderers! . . . Still, this is how it's done:

This is a war . . . But since these play, before they die,
Like puppies with their puppy; since, a man,
I did as these have done, but did not die —
I will content the people as I can
And give up these to them: Behold the man!

I have suffered, in a dream, because of him,
Many things; for this last savior, man,
I have lied as I lie now. But what is lying?
Men wash their hands, in blood, as best they can.
I find no fault in this just man.

THE GIFT OUTRIGHT
Robert Frost

The land was ours before we were the land's.
She was our land more than a hundred years
Before we were her people. She was ours
In Massachusetts, in Virginia,
But we were England's, still colonials,
Possessing what we still were unpossessed by,
Possessed by what we now no more possessed.
Something we were withholding made us weak
Until we found out that it was ourselves
We were withholding from our land of living,
And forthwith found salvation in surrender.
Such as we were we gave ourselves outright
(The deed of gift was many deeds of war)
To the land vaguely realizing westward,
But still unstoried, artless, unenhanced,
Such as she was, such as she would become.

POEMS OF THE CITY

ACQUAINTED WITH THE NIGHT
Robert Frost

I have been one acquainted with the night.
I have walked out in rain—and back in rain.
I have outwalked the furthest city light.

I have looked down the saddest city lane.
I have passed the watchman on his beat
And dropped my eyes, unwilling to explain.

I have stood still and stopped the sound of feet
When far away an interrupted cry
Came over houses from another street,

But not to call me back or say good-bye;
And further still at an unearthly height.
One luminary clock against the sky

Proclaimed the time was neither wrong nor right.
I have been one acquainted with the night.

PRAYERS OF STEEL
Carl Sandburg

Lay me on an anvil, O God.
Beat me and hammer me into a crowbar.
Let me pry loose old walls.
Let me lift and loosen old foundations.

Lay me on an anvil, O God.
Beat me and hammer me into a steel spike.
Drive me into the girders that hold a skyscraper together.
Take red-hot rivets and fasten me into the central girders.
Let me be the great nail holding a skyscraper through blue
     nights into white stars.

A FENCE
Carl Sandburg

Now the stone house on the lake front is finished and the
workmen are beginning the fence.
The palings are made of iron bars with steel points that can
stab the life out of any man who falls on them.
As a fence, it is a masterpiece, and will shut off the rabble
and all vagabonds and hungry men and all wandering
children looking for a place to play.
Passing through the bars and over the steel points will go
nothing except Death and the Rain and Tomorrow.

RIDING THE "A"

May Swenson

I ride
the "A" train
and feel
like a ball-
bearing in a roller skate.
I have on a gray
rain-
coat. The hollow
of the car
is gray.
My face
a negative in the slate
window,
I sit
in a lit
corridor that races
through a dark
one. Strok-
ing steel
what a smooth rasp—it feels

like the newest of knives
slicing
along
a long
black crusty loaf
from West 4th to 168th.
Wheels
and rails
in their prime
collide,
make love in a glide
of slickness
and friction.
It is an elation
I wish to pro-
long.
The station
is reached
too soon.

CONCRETE TRAP

Elizabeth Coatsworth

The fox at midnight in the city square
knows there's a way, but knows not which it is,
a path that leads to fields and woods and lair,
leaves underfoot, earth and the stirring air.
Bewildered stands the fox, too many streets
lead off too many ways, yet there is one
leads to the woods and to tomorrow's sun.
Under street lamps, between the straight house walls,
hard, geometric, baffling nose and eyes,
escape is there for him to recognize.
Bewildered stands the fox, questing the way,
and in yards the dogs begin to bay.

RAIN AFTER A VAUDEVILLE SHOW

Stephen Vincent Benét

The last pose flickered, failed. The screen's dead white
Glared in a sudden flooding of harsh light
Stabbing the eyes; and as I stumbled out
The curtain rose. A fat girl with a pout
And legs like hams, began to sing "His Mother."
Gusts of bad air rose in a choking smother;
Smoke, the wet steam of clothes, the stench of plush,
Powder, cheap perfume, mingled in a rush.
I stepped into the lobby—and stood still
Struck dumb by sudden beauty, body and will.
Cleanness and rapture—excellence made plain—
The storming, thrashing arrows of the rain!
Pouring and dripping on the roofs and rods,
Smelling of woods and hills and fresh-turned sods
Black on the sidewalks, grey in the far sky,
Crashing on thirsty panes, on gutters dry,
Hurrying the crowd to shelter, making fair
The streets, the houses, and the heat-soaked air,—
Merciful, holy, charging, sweeping, flashing,
It smote the soul with a most iron clashing! . . .
Like dragon's eyes the street-lamps suddenly gleamed,
Yellow and round and dim, low globes of flame.
And scarce-perceived, the clouds' tall banners streamed.
Out of the petty wars, the daily shame,
Beauty strove suddenly and rose, and flowered . . .
I gripped my coat and plunged where awnings lowered.
Made one with hissing blackness, caught, embraced,
By splendor and by striving and swift haste—
Spring coming in with thunderings and strife—
I stamped the ground in the strong joy of life.

GIVE ME THE SPLENDID SILENT SUN
Walt Whitman

I

Give me the splendid silent sun with all his beams full-
   dazzling,
Give me juicy autumnal fruit ripe and red from the orchard,
Give me a field where the unmowed grass grows,
Give me an arbor, give me the trellised grape,
Give me fresh corn and wheat, give me serene-moving animals
   teaching content,
Give me nights perfectly quiet as on high plateaus west of the
   Mississippi, and I looking up at the stars,
Give me odorous at sunrise a garden of beautiful flowers
   where I can walk undisturbed,
Give me for marriage a sweet-breathed woman of whom I
   should never tire,
Give me a perfect child, give me, away aside from the noise
   of the world, a rural domestic life,
Give me to warble spontaneous songs recluse by myself, for
   my own ears only,
Give me solitude, give me Nature, give me again O Nature
   your primal sanities!

These demanding to have them, (tired with ceaseless excite-
   ment and racked by the war-strife)
These to procure incessantly asking, rising in cries from my
   heart.
While yet incessantly asking still I adhere to my city,
Day upon day and year upon year, O city, walking your
   streets,
Where you hold me enchained a certain time refusing to give
   me up,
Yet giving to make me glutted, enriched of soul, you give me
   forever faces;
(O I see what I sought to escape, confronting, reversing my
   cries,
I see my own soul trampling down what it asked for.)

II

Keep your splendid silent sun,

Keep your woods, O Nature, and the quiet places by the woods,

Keep your fields of clover and timothy, and your cornfields and orchards,

Keep the blossoming buckwheat fields where the Ninth-month bees hum;

Give me faces and streets—give me these phantoms incessant and endless along the trottoirs!

Give me interminable eyes—give me women—give me comrades and lovers by the thousand!

Let me see new ones every day—let me hold new ones by the hand every day!

Give me such shows—give me the streets of Manhattan!

Give me Broadway, with the soldiers marching—give me the sound of the trumpets and drums!

(The soldiers in companies or regiments—some starting away flushed and reckless,

Some, their time up, returning with thinned ranks, young, yet very old, worn, marching, noticing nothing;)

Give me the shores and wharves heavy-fringed with black ships!

O such for me! O an intense life, full to repletion and varied!

The life of the theatre, bar-room, huge hotel, for me!

The saloon of the steamer! The crowded excursion for me! The torchlight procession!

The dense brigade bound for the war, with high-piled military wagons following;

People, endless, streaming, with strong voices, passions, pageants,

Manhattan streets with their powerful throbs, with beating drums as now,

The endless and noisy chorus, the rustle and clank of muskets (even the sight of the wounded),

Manhattan crowds, with their turbulent musical chorus!

Manhattan faces and eyes forever for me.

NIGHT GAME
Rolfe Humphries

Only bores are bored,—wrote William Saroyan—
And I was a bore, and so I went to the ball game;
But there was a pest who insisted on going with me.
I thought I could shake him if I bought one ticket,
But he must have come in on a pass. I couldn't see him,
But I knew he was there, back of third, in the row behind me,
His knees in my back, and his breath coming over my shoulder,
The loud-mouthed fool, the sickly nervous ego,
Repeating his silly questions, like a child
Or a girl at the first game ever. *Shut up*, I told him,
For Christ's sweet sake, shut up, and watch the ball game.
He didn't want to, but finally subsided,
And my attention found an outward focus,
Visible, pure, objective, inning by inning,
A well-played game, with no particular features,—
Feldman pitched well, and Ott hit a couple of homers.

And after the ninth, with the crowd in the bleachers, thinning,
And the lights in the grandstand dimming out behind us,
And a full moon hung before us, over the clubhouse,
I drifted out with the crowd across the diamond,
Over the infield brown and the smooth green outfield
So wonderful underfoot, so right, so perfect,
That each of us was a player for a moment,
The men my age, and the soldiers and the sailors,
Their girls, and the running kids, and the plodding old men,
Taking it easy, the same unhurried tempo,
In the mellow light and air, in the mild cool weather,
Moving together, moving out together,
Oh, this is good, I felt, to be part of this movement,
This mood, this music, part of the human race,
Alike and different, after the game is over,
Streaming away to the exit, and underground.

A SOLITUDE
Denise Levertov

A blind man. I can stare at him
ashamed, shameless. Or does he know it?
No, he is in a great solitude.

O, strange joy,
to gaze my fill at a stranger's face.
No, my thirst is greater than before.

In his world he is speaking
almost aloud. His lips move.
Anxiety plays about them. And now joy

of some sort trembles into a smile.
A breeze I can't feel
crosses that face as if it crossed water.

The train moves uptown, pulls in and
pulls out of the local stops. Within its loud
jarring movement a quiet,

the quiet of people not speaking,
some of them eyeing the blind man,
only a moment though, not thirsty like me,

and within that quiet, his
different quiet, not quiet at all, a tumult
of images, but what are his images,

he is blind? He doesn't care
that he looks strange, showing
his thoughts on his face like designs of light

flickering on water, for he doesn't know
what *look* is.
I see he has never seen.

And now he rises, he stands at the door ready,
knowing his station is next. Was he counting?
No, that was not his need.

When he gets out I get out.
"Can I help you towards the exit?"
"Oh, all right." An indifference.

But instantly, even as he speaks,
even as I hear indifference, his hand
goes out, waiting for me to take it,

and now we hold hands like children.
His hand is warm and not sweaty,
the grip firm, it feels good.

And when we have passed through the turnstile,
he going first, his hand at once
waits for mine again.

"Here are the steps. And here we turn
to the right. More stairs now." We go
up into sunlight. He feels that,

the soft air. "A nice day,
isn't it?" says the blind man. Solitude
walks with me, walks

beside me, he is not with me, he continues
his thoughts alone. But his hand and mine
know one another,

it's as if my hand were gone forth
on its own journey. I see him
across the street, the blind man,

and now he says he can find his way. He knows
where he is going, it is nowhere, it is filled
with presences. He says, *I am.*

SAL'S ATOMIC SUBMARINES
L.E. Sissman

The Puerto Rican busboy, Jesus, coughs
Above the cutting board where Sal compiles
An outboard order for the Abinger
Associates next door; then, carrying
A pantheon of heroes in a brown
Kraft-paper-bag, he sidles by the chrome-
Formica-plastic dinette furniture
And gains the world, where anti-personnel
Gases from crosstown buses, vegetable
Soup simmering at Bickford's and My Sin
Seeping from Walgreen's silently combine
To addle all outsiders. Only lithe,
Quick indigenes like Jesus (whose tan neck
Is thinner than my wrist) can long survive
And later even prosper in the air
Of these times' squares, these hexahedral hives
Where every worker drudges for his queen.

THE GOOD WILDERNESS

THE WAKING

Theodore Roethke

I strolled across
An open field;
The sun was out;
Heat was happy.

This way! This way!
The wren's throat shimmered,
Either to other,
The blossoms sang.

The stones sang,
The little ones did,
And flowers jumped
Like small goats.

A ragged fringe
Of daisies waved;
I wasn't alone
In a grove of apples.

Far in the wood
A nestling sighed;
The dew loosened
Its morning smells.

I came where the river
Ran over stones:
My ears knew
An early joy.

And all the waters
Of all the streams
Sang in my veins
That summer day.

THE GREAT SCARF OF BIRDS
John Updike

Playing golf on Cape Ann in October,
I saw something to remember.

Ripe apples were caught like red fish in the nets
of their branches. The maples
were colored like apples,
part orange and red, part green.
The elms, already transparent trees,
seemed swaying vases full of sky. The sky
was dramatic with great straggling V's
of geese streaming south, mare's tails above them.
Their trumpeting made us look up and around.
The course sloped into salt marshes,
and this seemed to cause the abundance of birds.

As if out of the Bible
of science fiction,
a cloud appeared, a cloud of dots
like iron filings which a magnet
underneath the paper undulates.
It dartingly darkened in spots,
paled, pulsed, compressed, distended, yet
held an identity firm: a flock
of starlings, as much one thing as a rock.
One will moved above the trees
the liquid and hesitant drift.

Come nearer, it became less marvellous,
more legible, and merely huge.
"I never saw so many birds!" my friend exclaimed.
We returned our eyes to the game.
Later, as Lot's wife must have done,
in a pause of walking, not thinking
of calling down a consequence,
I lazily looked around.

The rise of the fairway above us was tinted,
so evenly tinted I might not have noticed
but that at the rim of the delicate shadow
the starlings were thicker and outlined the flock
as an inkstain in drying pronounces its edges.
The gradual rise of green was vastly covered;
I had thought nothing in nature could be so broad but grass.

And as
I watched, one bird,
prompted by accident or will to lead,
ceased resting; and, lifting in a casual billow,
the flock ascended as a lady's scarf,
transparent, of gray, might be twitched
by one corner, drawn upward and then,
decided against, negligently tossed toward a chair:
the southward cloud withdrew into the air.

Long had it been since my heart
had been lifted as it was by the lifting of that great scarf.

THE RHODORA
On Being Asked, Whence Is the Flower?
Ralph Waldo Emerson

In May, when sea winds pierced our solitudes,
I found the fresh rhodora in the woods,
Spreading its leafless blooms in a damp nook,
To please the desert and the sluggish brook.
The purple petals, fallen in the pool,
Made the black water with their beauty gay;
Here might the redbird come his plumes to cool,
And court the flower that cheapens his array.
Rhodora! if the sages ask thee why
This charm is wasted on the earth and sky,
Tell them, dear, that if eyes were made for seeing,
Then Beauty is its own excuse for being:
Why thou wert there, O rival of the rose!
I never thought to ask, I never knew:
But, in my simple ignorance, suppose
The selfsame Power that brought me there brought you.

NEW HAMPSHIRE
Donald Hall

A bear sleeps in the cellar hole, where pine needles
heap over the granite doorstep. And the well brims
with acorns and the broken leaves of the oak tree
that has grown where the anvil rusted in the forge.

When my eyes close, I can see another summer:
a bark of rust grows on the trees of the gas pumps,
and the EAT signs gather like leaves in the shallow
cellars of diners, and a wildcat waits for deer

on the roof of a car. Blacktop buckled by frost
starts goldenrod from the highway. Fat honey bees
meander among raspberries, where a quarrel
of vines crawls into the spilled body of a plane.

SANDPIPERS

Howard Nemerov

In the small territory and time
Between one wave and the next, they run
Down the beach and back, eating things
Which seem, conveniently for them,
To surface only when the sand gets wet.
Small, dapper birds, they make me think
Of commuters seen, say, in an early movie,
Where the rough screen wavers, where the light
Jerks and seems to rain; of clockwork dolls
Set going on the sidewalk, drawing a crowd
Beside the newsstand at five o'clock, their legs
Black toothpicks, their heads nodding at nothing.
But this comedy is based upon exact
Perceptions, and delicately balanced
Between starvation and the sea—
Though sometimes I have seen one slip and fall
From either the undertow or greed
And have to get up in the wave's open mouth,
Still eating. I have never seen
One caught; if necessary, he spreads his wings,
With the white stripe, and flutters rather than flies
Out to begin eating again at once.
Now they are over every outer beach,
Procrastinating steadily southward
In endlessly local comings and goings.

Whenever a flock of them takes flight
And flies with the beautiful ùnison
Of banners in the wind, they are
No longer funny. It is their courage,
Meaningless as the word is when compared
With their thoughtless precisions, that strikes
Me when I watch them hidden and revealed
Between two waves, lost in the sea's
Lost color as they distance me — flying
From winter already, while I
Am in August. When suddenly they turn
In unison, all their bellies shining
Like mirrors white with flashing signals
I cannot read, I wish them well.

EEL-GRASS
Edna St. Vincent Millay

No matter what I say,
    All that I really love
Is the rain that flattens on the bay,
    And the eel-grass in the cove;
The jingle-shells that lie and bleach
    At the tide-line, and the trace
Of higher tides along the beach:
    Nothing in this place.

WHAT'S THE RAILROAD TO ME?
Henry David Thoreau

What's the railroad to me?
I never go to see
Where it ends.
It fills a few hollows,
And makes banks for the swallows,
It sets the sand a-blowing,
And the blackberries a-growing.

THE FLOWER-FED BUFFALOES
Vachel Lindsay

The flower-fed buffaloes of the spring
In the days of long ago,
Ranged where the locomotives sing
And the prairie flowers lie low;
The tossing, blooming, perfumed grass
Is swept away by wheat,
Wheat and wheels and wheels spin by
In the spring that still is sweet.
But the flower-fed buffaloes of the spring
Left us long ago.
They gore no more, they bellow no more,
They trundle around the hills no more:—
With the Blackfeet lying low,
With the Pawnees lying low.

TRAVELING THROUGH THE DARK
William Stafford

Traveling through the dark I found a deer
dead on the edge of the Wilson River road.
It is usually best to roll them into the canyon:
that road is narrow; to swerve might make more dead.

By glow of the tail-light I stumbled back of the car
and stood by the heap, a doe, a recent killing;
she had stiffened already, almost cold.
I dragged her off; she was large in the belly.

My fingers touching her side brought me the reason —
her side was warm; her fawn lay there waiting,
alive, still, never to be born.
Beside that mountain road I hesitated.

The car aimed ahead its lowered parking lights;
under the hood purred the steady engine.
I stood in the glare of the warm exhaust turning red;
around our group I could hear the wilderness listen.

I thought hard for us all — my only swerving —
then pushed her over the edge into the river.

ABOVE PATE VALLEY

Gary Snyder

We finished clearing the last
Section of trail by noon,
High on the ridge-side
Two thousand feet above the creek—
Reached the pass, went on
Beyond the white pine groves,
Granite shoulders, to a small
Green meadow watered by the snow,
Edged with Aspen—sun
Straight high and blazing
But the air was cool.
Ate a cold fried trout in the
Trembling shadows. I spied
A glitter, and found a flake
Black volcanic glass—obsidian—
By a flower. Hands and knees
Pushing the Bear grass, thousands
Of arrowhead leavings over a
Hundred yards. Not one good
Head, just razor flakes
On a hill snowed all but summer,
A land of fat summer deer,
They came to camp. On their
Own trails. I followed my own
Trail here. Picked up the cold-drill,
Pick, singlejack, and sack
Of dynamite.
Ten thousand years.

THERE WAS A TIME
Elizabeth Coatsworth

There was a time I used to think
a Persian sunset flushing pink
was beautiful — now I prefer
say an old marsh with ruffled fur
and stranded branches, bleached and queer,
like antlers of some mythic deer.

FLOWERS BY THE SEA
William Carlos Williams

When over the flowery, sharp pasture's
edge, unseen, the salt ocean

lifts its form — chickory and daisies
tied, released, seem hardly flowers alone

but color and the movement — or the shape
perhaps — of restlessness whereas

the sea is circled and sways
peacefully upon its plantlike stem

MORE FIGURATIVELY

IN A STATION OF THE METRO
Ezra Pound

The apparition of these faces in the crowd;
Petals on a wet, black bough.

HOKKU
Richard Wright

In the falling snow
A laughing boy holds out his palms
Until they are white

FOG
Carl Sandburg

The fog comes
on little cat feet.

It sits looking
over harbor and city
on silent haunches
and then moves on.

BIRCHES
Robert Frost

When I see birches bend to left and right
Across the lines of straighter darker trees,
I like to think some boy's been swinging them.
But swinging doesn't bend them down to stay
As ice-storms do. Often you must have seen them
Loaded with ice a sunny winter morning
After a rain. They click upon themselves
As the breeze rises, and turn many-colored
As the stir cracks and crazes their enamel.
Soon the sun's warmth makes them shed crystal shells
Shattering and avalanching on the snow-crust—
Such heaps of broken glass to sweep away
You'd think the inner dome of heaven had fallen.
They are dragged to the withered bracken by the load,
And they seem not to break; though once they are bowed
So low for long, they never right themselves:
You may see their trunks arching in the woods
Years afterwards, trailing their leaves on the ground
Like girls on hands and knees that throw their hair
Before them over their heads to dry in the sun.
But I was going to say when Truth broke in
With all her matter-of-fact about the ice-storm
I should prefer to have some boy bend them
As he went out and in to fetch the cows—
Some boy too far from town to learn baseball,
Whose only play was what he found himself,
Summer or winter, and could play alone.
One by one he subdued his father's trees
By riding them down over and over again

Until he took the stiffness out of them,
And not one but hung limp, not one was left
For him to conquer. He learned all there was
To learn about not launching out too soon
And so not carrying the tree away
Clear to the ground. He always kept his poise
To the top branches, climbing carefully
With the same pains you use to fill a cup
Up to the brim, and even above the brim.
Then he flung outward, feet first, with a swish,
Kicking his way down through the air to the ground.
So was I once myself a swinger of birches.
And so I dream of going back to be.
It's when I'm weary of considerations,
And life is too much like a pathless wood
Where your face burns and tickles with the cobwebs
Broken across it, and one eye is weeping
From a twig's having lashed across it open.
I'd like to get away from earth awhile
And then come back to it and begin over.
May no fate willfully misunderstand me
And half grant what I wish and snatch me away
Not to return. Earth's the right place for love:
I don't know where it's likely to go better.
I'd like to go by climbing a birch tree,
And climb black branches up a snow-white trunk
Toward heaven, till the tree could bear no more,
But dipped its top and set me down again.
That would be good both going and coming back.
One could do worse than be a swinger of birches.

WIND AND SILVER
Amy Lowell

Greatly shining,
The Autumn moon floats in the thin sky;
And the fish-ponds shake their backs and flash their dragon
    scales
As she passes over them.

NIGHT CLOUDS
Amy Lowell

The white mares of the moon rush along the sky
Beating their golden hoofs upon the glass Heavens;
The white mares of the moon are all standing on their hind
    legs
Pawing at the green porcelain doors of the remote Heavens.
Fly, Mares!
Strain your utmost,
Scatter the milky dust of stars,
Or the tiger sun will leap upon you and destroy you
With one lick of his vermilion tongue.

BIG WIND
Theodore Roethke

Where were the greenhouses going,
Lunging into the lashing
Wind driving water
So far down the river
All the faucets stopped? —
So we drained the manure-machine
For the steam plant,
Pumping the stale mixture
Into the rusty boilers,
Watching the pressure gauge
Waver over to red,
As the seams hissed
And the live steam
Drove to the far
End of the rose-house,
Where the worst wind was,
Creaking the cypress window-frames,
Cracking so much thin glass
We stayed all night,
Stuffing the holes with burlap;
But she rode it out,
That old rose-house,
She hove into the teeth of it,
The core and pith of that ugly storm,
Ploughing with her stiff prow,
Bucking into the wind-waves
That broke over the whole of her,
Flailing her sides with spray,
Flinging long strings of wet across the rooftop,
Finally veering, wearing themselves out, merely
Whistling thinly under the wind-vents;
She sailed into the calm morning,
Carrying her full cargo of roses.

THE NOVEMBER SHINE
Rolfe Humphries

Not now the oil-black shimmer of summer on the road,
But a gray glare, still glare, though, and still bright
Enough to narrow eyes against. We smell
The smoke, again, of burning leaves — how trite
A thing to say, or notice! — and the car
Swings to the left-hand lane, and on our right
We pass a truck, two kids in the back, and one
A tow-head, with a casque of shining white.
The road-side stands have rows of pumpkins, late,
Too late for Hallowe'en, too small for suns,
But huge for pumpkins, seamed and orange, burning
Beside the smoother cider — jars, whose light
Flashes an amber dazzle, lamps in day-time.
With the leaves gone, or almost, sunlight blinds,
Reflected from smooth bark or bough, and sky
Is quiet gray-blue lake, or bay, as far as eye
Can see, or tell. Less color, to be sure,
Less warmth, no heavy shade, less green, but still
Not yet enough of sharpness nor of chill
To shiver for, or wind the windows tight.
So far, November's need supplies its answer —
More light, more light.

CAT ON A COUCH
Barbara Howes

My cat, washing her tail's tip, is a whorl
Of white shell,
As perfect as a fan
In full half-moon . . . Next moment she's a hare:
The muzzle softens, rounds, goes dumb, and one
Tall ear dips, falters forward . . . Then,
Cross as switches, she's a great horned owl;
Two leafy tricorned ears reverse, a frown
Darkens her chalky visage, big eyes round
And round and stare down midnight. There sits my cat

Mysterious as gauze,—now somnolent,
Now jocose, quicksilver from a dropped
Thermometer. When poised
Below the sketched ballet—
Dancers who pirouette upon the wall,
Calmly she lifts the slim
Boom of her leg, what will
The prima ballerina next
Perform?—Grace held in readiness,
She meditates, a vision of repose.

TELEPHONE POLES
John Updike

They have been with us a long time.
They will outlast the elms.
Our eyes, like the eyes of a savage sieving the trees
In search for game,
Run through them. They blend along small town streets
Like a race of giants that have faded into mere mythology.
Our eyes, washed clean of belief,
Lift incredulous to their fearsome crowns of bolts, trusses,
  struts, nuts, insulators, and such
Barnacles as compose
These weathered encrustations of electrical debris—
Each a Gorgon's head, which, seized right,
Could stun us to stone.

Yet they are ours. We made them.
See here, where the cleats of linemen
Have roughened a second bark
Onto the bald trunk. And these spikes
Have been driven sideways at intervals handy for human legs.
The Nature of our construction is in every way
A better fit than the Nature it displaces.
What other tree can you climb where the birds' twitter,
Unscrambled, is English? True, their thin shade is negligible,
But then again there is not that tragic autumnal
Casting-off of leaves to outface annually.
These giants are more constant than evergreens
By being never green.

FIRST LESSON
Philip Booth

Lie back, daughter, let your head
be tipped back in the cup of my hand.
Gently, and I will hold you. Spread
your arms wide, lie out on the stream
and look high at the gulls. A dead-
man's float is face down. You will dive
and swim soon enough where this tidewater
ebbs to the sea. Daughter, believe
me, when you tire on the long thrash
to your island, lie up, and survive.
As you float now, where I held you
and let you go, remember when fear
cramps your heart what I told you:
lie gently and wide to the light-year
stars, lie back, and the sea will hold you.

VOYAGES I

Hart Crane

Above the fresh ruffles of the surf
Bright striped urchins flay each other with sand.
They have contrived a conquest for shell shucks,
And their fingers crumble fragments of baked weed
Gaily digging and scattering.

And in answer to their treble interjections
The sun beats lightning on the waves,
The waves fold thunder on the sand;
And could they hear me I would tell them:

O brilliant kids, frisk with your dog,
Fondle your shells and sticks, bleached
By time and the elements; but there is a line
You must not cross nor ever trust beyond it
Spry cordage of your bodies to caresses
Too lichen-faithful from too wide a breast.
The bottom of the sea is cruel.

FIRE AND ICE
Robert Frost

Some say the world will end in fire,
Some say in ice.
From what I've tasted of desire
I hold with those who favor fire.
But if it had to perish twice,
I think I know enough of hate
To say that for destruction ice
Is also great
And would suffice.

THE MARSH
W. D. Snodgrass

Swampstrife and spatterdock
   lull in the heavy waters;
some thirty little frogs
   spring with each step you walk;
a fish's belly glitters
   tangled by rotting logs.

Over near the grey rocks
   muskrats dip and circle.
Out of his rim of ooze
   a silt-black pond snail walks
inverted on the surface
   toward what food he may choose.

You look up; while you walk
   the sun bobs and is snarled
in the enclosing weir
   of trees, in their dead stalks.
Stick in the mud, old heart,
   what are you doing here?

THE HERON
Raymond Holden

How would it be to have an eye
That did not know this water contained sky;
That could not wisely winnow
Globed cloud from green frog and pearl dappled minnow?
Busy with his infinite stillness stands
The heron who wears wings where men have hands.
The instinctive orderliness of his lack of thought
Keeps him from being distraught.
He does not, we suppose, confuse
Snakes and salamanders with the latest news,
Nor fly because to do so makes him feel
Superior and godlike and unreal.
How would it be to know delight
Without a name for it; to know night
From day only by its shutting out of fish
From the marsh's silver-shallow dish?
How would it be not to know what love
Is the appellation of;
To have no consciousness of death
And so to live as if a heron's blood and breath
And the tissues which they lace
Were endless as the wordlessness of space?

LIMITED
Carl Sandburg

I am riding on a limited express, one of the crack trains of
the nation.
Hurtling across the prairie into blue haze and dark air go
fifteen all-steel coaches holding a thousand people.
(All the coaches shall be scrap and rust and all the men and
women laughing in the diners and sleepers shall pass to
ashes.)
I ask a man in the smoker where he is going and he answers:
"Omaha."

NOTHING GOLD CAN STAY
Robert Frost

Nature's first green is gold,
Her hardest hue to hold,
Her early leaf's a flower;
But only so an hour.
Then leaf subsides to leaf.
So Eden sank to grief,
So dawn goes down to day.
Nothing gold can stay.

THE DAY
Theodore Spencer

The day was a year at first
When children ran in the garden;
The day shrank down to a month
When the boys played ball.

The day was a week thereafter
When young men walked in the garden;
The day was itself a day
When love grew tall.

The day shrank down to an hour
When old men limped in the garden;
The day will last forever
When it is nothing at all.

FARTHER
OUT

THE ROPEWALK

Henry Wadsworth Longfellow

In that building, long and low,
With its windows all a-row,
   Like the port-holes of a hulk,
Human spiders spin and spin,
Backward down their threads so thin
   Dropping, each a hempen bulk.

At the end, an open door;
Squares of sunshine on the floor
   Light the long and dusky lane;
And the whirring of a wheel,
Dull and drowsy, makes me feel
   All its spokes are in my brain.

As the spinners to the end
Downward go and reascend,
   Gleam the long threads in the sun;
While within this brain of mine
Cobwebs brighter and more fine
   By the busy wheel are spun.

Two fair maidens in a swing,
Like white doves upon the wing,
   First before my vision pass;
Laughing, as their gentle hands
Closely clasp the twisted strands,
   At their shadow on the grass.

Then a booth of mountebanks,
With its smell of tan and planks,
   And a girl poised high in air
On a cord, in spangled dress,
With a faded loveliness,
   And a weary look of care.

Then a homestead among farms,
And a woman with bare arms
    Drawing water from a well;
As the bucket mounts apace,
With it mounts her own fair face,
    As at some magician's spell.

Then an old man in a tower,
Ringing loud the noontide hour,
    While the rope coils round and round
Like a serpent at his feet,
And again, in swift retreat,
    Nearly lifts him from the ground.

Then within a prison-yard,
Faces fixed, and stern, and hard,
    Laughter and indecent mirth;
Ah! it is the gallows-tree!
Breath of Christian charity,
    Blow, and sweep it from the earth!

Then a school-boy, with his kite
Gleaming in a sky of light,
    And an eager, upward look;
Steeds pursued through lane and field;
Fowlers with their snares concealed;
    And an angler by a brook.

Ships rejoicing in the breeze,
Wrecks that float o'er unknown seas,
    Anchors dragged through faithless sand;
Sea-fog drifting overhead,
And, with lessening line and lead,
    Sailors feeling for the land.

All these scenes do I behold,
These, and many left untold,
   In that building long and low;
While the wheel goes round and round,
With a drowsy, dreamy sound,
   And the spinners backward go.

LITTLE ELEGY
for a child who skipped rope
X. J. Kennedy

Here lies resting, out of breath,
Out of turns, Elizabeth
Whose quicksilver toes not quite
Cleared the whirring edge of night.

Earth whose circles round us skim
Till they catch the lightest limb,
Shelter now Elizabeth
And for her sake trip up death.

SALEM

Robert Lowell

In Salem seasick spindrift drifts or skips
To the canvas flapping on the seaward panes
Until the knitting sailor stabs at ships
Nosing like sheep of Morpheus through his brain's
Asylum. Seaman, seaman, how the draft
Lashes the oily slick about your head,
Beating up whitecaps! Seaman, Charon's raft
Dumps its damned goods into the harbor-bed,—
There sewage sickens the rebellious seas.
Remember, seaman, Salem fishermen
Once hung their nimble fleets on the Great Banks.
Where was it that New England bred the men
Who quartered the Leviathan's fat flanks
And fought the British Lion to his knees?

ORIENT WHEAT

Adrienne Rich

Our fathers in their books and speech
Have made the matter plain:
The green fields they walked in once
Will never grow again.
The corn lies under the locust's tooth
Or blistered in the sun;
The faces of the old proud stock
Are gone where their years are gone.

The park where stags lay down at noon
Under the great trees
Is shrill with Sunday strollers now,
Littered with their lees.
Poachers have trampled down the maze
And choked the fountains dry;
The last swan of a score and ten
Goes among reeds to die.

We were born to smells of plague,
Chalk-marks on every door;
We never have heard the hunting-horn
Or feet on the gallery floor—
The high-arched feet of dancers
Who knew how to step and stand.
We were born of a leaning house
In a changed, uneasy land.

Our fathers curse the crooked time
And go to their graves at last;
While some of us laugh at doting men,
And others sigh for the past.
And the dazzled lovers lie
Where summer burns blue and green,
In the green fields they'll be saying
Can never grow again.

I MET A SEER

Stephen Crane

I met a seer.
He held in his hands
The book of wisdom.
"Sir," I addressed him,
"Let me read."
"Child—" he began.
"Think not that I am a child,
For already I know much
Of that which you hold.
Ay, much."

He smiled.
Then he opened the book
And held it before me.—
Strange that I should have grown so suddenly blind.

A YOUTH IN APPAREL
THAT GLITTERED

Stephen Crane

A youth in apparel that glittered
Went to walk in a grim forest.
There he met an assassin
Attired all in garb of old days;
He, scowling through the thickets,
And dagger poised quivering,
Rushed upon the youth.
"Sir," said this latter,
"I am enchanted, believe me,
To die, thus,
In this medieval fashion,
According to the best legends;
Ah, what joy!"
Then took he the wound, smiling,
And died, content.

CLIFF KLINGENHAGEN
Edwin Arlington Robinson

Cliff Klingenhagen had me in to dine
With him one day; and after soup and meat,
And all the other things there were to eat,
Cliff took two glasses and filled one with wine
And one with wormwood. Then, without a sign
For me to choose at all, he took the draught
Of bitterness himself, and lightly quaffed
It off, and said the other one was mine.

And when I asked him what the deuce he meant
By doing that, he only looked at me
And smiled, and said it was a way of his.
And though I know the fellow, I have spent
Long time a-wondering when I shall be
As happy as Cliff Klingenhagen is.

BOATS IN A FOG
Robinson Jeffers

Sports and gallantries, the stage, the arts, the antics of dancers,
The exuberant voices of music,
Have charm for children but lack nobility; it is bitter earnest-
     ness
That makes beauty; the mind
Knows, grown adult.
                         A sudden fog-drift muffled the ocean,
A throbbing of engines moved in it,
At length, a stone's throw out, between the rocks and vapor,
One by one moved shadows
Out of the mystery, shadows, fishing-boats, trailing each
     other,
Following the cliff for guidance,
Holding a difficult path between the peril of the sea-fog
And the foam on the shore granite.
One by one, trailing their leader, six crept by me,
Out of the vapor and into it,
The throb of their engines subdued by the fog, patient and
     cautious,
Coasting all around the peninsula
Back to the buoys in Monterey harbor. A flight of pelicans
Is nothing lovelier to look at;
The flight of the planets is nothing nobler; all the arts lose
     virtue
Against the essential reality
Of creatures going about their business among the equally
Earnest elements of nature.

DAYS
Ralph Waldo Emerson

Daughters of Time, the hypocritic Days,
Muffled and dumb like barefoot dervishes,
And marching single in an endless file,
Bring diadems and fagots in their hands.
To each they offer gifts after his will,
Bread, kingdoms, stars, and sky that holds them all.
I, in my pleached garden, watched the pomp,
Forgot my morning wishes, hastily
Took a few herbs and apples, and the Day
Turned and departed silent. I, too late,
Under her solemn fillet saw the scorn.

JUGGLER
Richard Wilbur

A ball will bounce, but less and less. It's not
A lighthearted thing, resents its own resilience.
Falling is what it loves, and the earth falls
So in our hearts from brilliance,
Settles and is forgot.
It takes a sky-blue juggler with five red balls

To shake our gravity up. Whee, in the air
The balls roll round, wheel on his wheeling hands,
Learning the ways of lightness, alter to spheres
Grazing his finger ends,
Cling to their courses there,
Swinging a small heaven about his ears.

But a heaven is easier made of nothing at all
Than the earth regained, and still and sole within
The spin of worlds, with a gesture sure and noble
He reels that heaven in,
Landing it ball by ball,
And trades it all for a broom, a plate, a table.

Oh, on his toe the table is turning, the broom's
Balancing up on his nose, and the plate whirls
On the tip of the broom! Damn, what a show, we cry:
The boys stamp, and the girls
Shriek, and the drum booms
And all comes down, and he bows and says good-bye.

If the juggler is tired now, if the broom stands
In the dust again, if the table starts to drop
Through the daily dark again, and though the plate
Lies flat on the table top,
For him we batter our hands
Who has won for once over the world's weight.

BRAHMA

Ralph Waldo Emerson

If the red slayer think he slays,
   Or if the slain think he is slain,
They know not well the subtle ways
   I keep, and pass, and turn again.

Far or forgot to me is near;
   Shadow and sunlight are the same;
The vanquished gods to me appear;
   And one to me are shame and fame.

They reckon ill who leave me out;
   When me they fly, I am the wings;
I am the doubter and the doubt,
   And I the hymn the Brahmin sings.

The strong gods pine for my abode,
   And pine in vain the sacred Seven;
But thou, meek lover of the good!
   Find me, and turn thy back on heaven.

THE GODDESS
Denise Levertov

She in whose lip service
I passed my time,
whose name I knew, but not her face
came upon me where I lay in Lie Castle!

Flung me across the room, and
room after room (hitting the wall, re-
bounding—to the last
sticky wall—wrenching away from it
pulled hair out!)
till I lay outside the outer walls!

There in cold air
lying still where her hand had thrown me,
I tasted the mud that splattered my lips:
the seeds of a forest were in it,
asleep and growing! I tasted
her power!

The silence was answering my silence,
a forest was pushing itself
out of sleep between my submerged fingers.
I bit on a seed and it spoke on my tongue
of day that shone already among stars
in the water-mirror of low ground,

and a wind rising ruffled the lights:
she passed near me returning from the encounter,
she who plucked me from the close rooms,

without whom nothing
flowers, fruits, sleeps in season,
without whom nothing
speaks in its own tongue, but returns
lie for lie!

STOPPING BY WOODS
ON A SNOWY EVENING
Robert Frost

Whose woods these are I think I know.
His house is in the village though;
He will not see me stopping here
To watch his woods fill up with snow.

My little horse must think it queer
To stop without a farmhouse near
Between the woods and frozen lake
The darkest evening of the year.

He gives his harness bells a shake
To ask if there is some mistake.
The only other sound's the sweep
Of easy wind and downy flake.

The woods are lovely, dark and deep.
But I have promises to keep,
And miles to go before I sleep,
And miles to go before I sleep.

THE SHEAVES
Edwin Arlington Robinson

Where long the shadows of the wind had rolled,
Green wheat was yielding to the change assigned;
And as by some vast magic undivined
The world was turning slowly into gold.
Like nothing that was ever bought or sold
It waited there, the body and the mind;
And with a mighty meaning of a kind
That tells the more the more it is not told.

So in a land where all days are not fair,
Fair days went on till on another day
A thousand golden sheaves were lying there,
Shining and still, but not for long to stay —
As if a thousand girls with golden hair
Might rise from where they slept and go away.

ELDORADO
Edgar Allan Poe

Gaily bedight,
A gallant knight,
In sunshine and in shadow,
Had journeyed long,
Singing a song,
In search of Eldorado.

But he grew old —
This knight so bold —
And o'er his heart a shadow
Fell as he found
No spot of ground
That looked like Eldorado.

And, as his strength
Failed him at length,
He met a pilgrim shadow —
"Shadow," said he,
"Where can it be —
This land of Eldorado?"

"Over the Mountains
Of the Moon,
Down the Valley of the Shadow,
Ride, boldly ride,"
The shade replied —
"If you seek for Eldorado."

FIRST SONG
Galway Kinnell

Then it was dusk in Illinois, the small boy
After an afternoon of carting dung
Hung on the rail fence, a sapped thing
Weary to crying. Dark was growing tall
And he began to hear the pond frogs all
Calling upon his ear with what seemed their joy.

Soon their sound was pleasant for a boy
Listening in the smoky dusk and the nightfall
Of Illinois, and then from the field two small
Boys came bearing cornstalk violins
And rubbed three cornstalk bows with resins,
And they set fiddling with them as with joy.

It was now fine music the frogs and the boys
Did in the towering Illinois twilight make
And into dark in spite of a right arm's ache
A boy's hunched body loved out of a stalk
The first song of his happiness, and the song woke
His heart to the darkness and into the sadness of joy.

THE ROAD NOT TAKEN
Robert Frost

Two roads diverged in a yellow wood,
And sorry I could not travel both
And be one traveler, long I stood
And looked down one as far as I could
To where it bent in the undergrowth;

Then took the other, as just as fair,
And having perhaps the better claim,
Because it was grassy and wanted wear;
Though as for that the passing there
Had worn them really about the same,

And both that morning equally lay
In leaves no step had trodden black.
Oh, I kept the first for another day!
Yet knowing how way leads on to way,
I doubted if I should ever come back.

I shall be telling this with a sigh
Somewhere ages and ages hence:
Two roads diverged in a wood, and I —
I took the one less traveled by,
And that has made all the difference.

THE POEM
Donald Hall

It discovers by night
what the day hid from it.
Sometimes it turns itself
into an animal.
In summer it takes long walks
by itself where meadows
fold back from ditches.
Once it stood still
in a quiet row of machines.
Who knows
what it is thinking?

NOTES ON THE POEMS

PEOPLE, GROUP ONE

THE GUM-GATHERER, Robert Frost, p. 16.
In this poem Frost is talking about the gum obtained from
spruce trees. This kind of gum is hard to find in most stores,
but it can be ordered from Five Islands, Georgetown, Maine.
grist (14): broken-off rock.
stolen shack (20): hidden, secret hut.

MY PAPA'S WALTZ, Theodore Roethke, p. 18.
The poet's last name is pronounced *Ret·key*.

THE CENTAUR, May Swenson, p. 19.
Centaur: In Greek mythology a centaur is a creature that
is half man and half horse.

MINIVER CHEEVY, Edwin Arlington Robinson, p. 23.
Thebes (11): ancient Egyptian city on the Nile.
Camelot (11): legendary English town where King Arthur
and his Knights of the Round Table held court.
Priam (12): the last king of Troy, and father of Hector and
Paris.
now on the town (15): dependent on public charity.
Medici (17): powerful Renaissance family of bankers and
princes in Florence, Italy.
khaki (22): color of army uniforms.

iron clothing (24): medieval armor.

Robinson's poetry falls into two groups: 1) long narrative poems on historical themes and 2) character portraits, probing with psychological insight into lives of frustration, defeat, and loneliness. Many of the character portraits are of New Englanders, inhabitants of Tilbury Town, an imaginary village based on Robinson's own boyhood home town, Gardiner, Maine. "Miniver Cheevy" is one of Robinson's character portraits.

GEORGE GRAY, Edgar Lee Masters, p. 24.

"George Gray," "Lucinda Matlock," "William Goode," and "Fiddler Jones" are from Masters' *Spoon River Anthology*. In each of the two hundred forty-four free-verse poems in the anthology, an ex-inhabitant of the town of Spoon River speaks from the grave and tells the inner truth of his or her life. Notice that George Gray begins this poem by talking about the epitaph carved on his tombstone.

LUCINDA MATLOCK, Edgar Lee Masters, p. 25.

degenerate (20): inferior or immoral.

FIDDLER JONES, Edgar Lee Masters, p. 27.

beeves (8): beef cattle.

"Toor-a-Loor" (14): American folk song.

till my forty acres (15): cultivate his small farm, probably one quarter of the one-hundred-sixty-acre parcels offered free by the federal government to any bona fide settler in accordance with the terms of the Homestead Act of 1862.

EX-BASKETBALL PLAYER, John Updike, p. 28.

tiers (29): rows or ranks arranged one above another.

Necco Wafers, Nibs, and Juju Beads (30): inexpensive candies, colorfully packaged.

KING JUKE, Kenneth Fearing, p. 29.

the jukebox eats live nickels raw (5): it only cost five cents to

play a jukebox in the early 1940s when this poem was
written.

fingers of steel (13): the mechanism for clasping a record and
moving it onto the turntable.

ALIVE AND SPOKEN, GROUP TWO

APHRODITE AS HISTORY, Robert Francis, p. 31.

Aphrodite: Greek goddess of love.

Praxiteles (5): considered to be the greatest Greek sculptor
in the fourth century B.C.

Robert Francis said in a television interview in 1966 that
he began this poem in the Metropolitan Museum of Art in
New York City while standing before a statue of Aphrodite
and reading its label, which stated:

> "MARBLE STATUE OF APHRODITE — Roman copy
> of a lost Greek original of about 300 B.C. The Greek orig-
> inal was made by an unknown sculptor working in the
> immediate tradition of the Cnidian Aphrodite by Praxi-
> teles. Probably found in or near Rome in the XVIII
> century."

REASON, Josephine Miles, p. 34.

On first reading this poem you may be slightly bewildered
because the poet does not use quotation marks and does not
identify who is speaking, except in the third speech where
the words are attributed to the usher. After several readings
you undoubtedly will realize that the narrator is the second
speaker and that he is in the head car. The setting, as the
reference to the usher and to movie star Gary Cooper indicate, is in front of a movie theatre.

Josephine Miles has explained why this is one of her
favorite poems: "because I like the idea of speech — not
images, not ideas, not music, but people talking — as the
material from which poetry is made. . . . I like the spare
and active interplay of talk."

COBB WOULD HAVE CAUGHT IT,
Robert Fitzgerald, p. 37.

Cobb: Ty Cobb (1886-1961) outfielder with the Detroit Tigers for more than twenty years. Had .367 lifetime batting average; led American league in batting twelve times and created or equaled more major league records than any other player.

casque (12): helmet.

before it ducks (18): before the pitcher's curve ball breaks.

HAY FOR THE HORSES, Gary Snyder, p. 38.

San Joaquin (2): the name of a river and of a county in California.

Mariposa (3): the name of a county in California and of a village in that county.

THE MOST OF IT, Robert Frost, p. 39.

The title is short for "making the most of it"; in other words, accepting the reality of the matter. Frost's wife died in 1938, and it is believed that this poem was written around 1940.

talus (11): rock fragments.

PITY THIS BUSY MONSTER MANUNKIND,
E. E. Cummings, p. 40.

The emphasis in the first two lines of the poem is on the first word in the second line: *not*. Cummings is saying do not pity this busy monster manunkind.

manunkind (1): this word combines *unkind* in the sense of harsh and *unkind* in the sense of unnatural or contrary to one's kind.

electrons . . . mountainrange (5-6): razor blades are enormously enlarged on the television screen.

lenses extend unwish through curving (6-7): giant telescopes explore Einstein's theory of time and space.

THE EMPEROR OF ICE CREAM, Wallace Stevens, p. 41.

fantails (11): fantail pigeons.

Of this poem, poet Donald Hall once said: "It will be puzzling if you ask the wrong questions of it. A woman is dead and her acquaintances mourn her. As for the emperor of ice cream—he is just the emperor of ice cream, that's all."

In 1933, Wallace Stevens himself chose this poem as his favorite, with the comment that the poem "wears a deliberately commonplace costume, and yet it seems to me to contain something of the essential gaudiness of poetry." Elsewhere Stevens wrote that "the true sense of *Let be be the finale of seem* is *let being become the conclusion or denouement of appearing to be:* in short ice cream is an absolute good. The poem is obviously not about ice cream, but about *being* as distinguished from *seeming to be*" *(Letter to Henry Church, June 1, 1939).*

LOVE POEMS, GROUP THREE

A DECADE, Amy Lowell, p. 43.
   morning bread (3): bread freshly baked at home before breakfast.

COOL TOMBS, Carl Sandburg, p. 46.
   copperhead (1): 1) a poisonous snake; 2) a nickname given to Northerners who sympathized with the South in the Civil War.
   the assassin (1): Lincoln was assassinated by John Wilkes Booth, an actor.
   con men (2): slang for swindlers who first gain the victim's *con*fidence.
   Grant, 18th President of the U.S., though honest himself, associated with disreputable politicians and financiers whose speculations led to the crash of 1873 and the closing of the New York Stock Exchange.
   Pocahontas (3): American Indian princess (1595?-1616), said to have saved Captain John Smith from execution in Virginia.

red haw (3): berry of the hawthorn tree.

pawpaw (3): common name for the papaya tree, or for its fruit.

ANNE RUTLEDGE, Edgar Lee Masters, p. 47.

Anne Rutledge: a young woman from New Salem, Illinois. She was to have married Abraham Lincoln but died when she was only nineteen years old.

vibrations of deathless music (2): Lincoln's eloquent and famous statements.

"With malice toward none, with charity for all" (3): words from Lincoln's Second Inaugural Address, given March 4, 1865, barely a month before Lee's surrender at Appomattox.

THE FIRE OF DRIFT-WOOD,
Henry Wadsworth Longfellow, p. 48.

Notice that the poem builds throughout to the beautiful outer-inner balance expressed in the final four lines: outside, the blazing fire of driftwood; inside, the burning thoughts of lost love.

THE RIVER-MERCHANT'S WIFE: A LETTER; Li Po;
Ezra Pound, translator, p. 51.

Ezra Pound, the translator of this poem, was a superb craftsman and student of languages. Among his great contributions to modern poetry are the translations into English of Oriental and medieval European and Anglo-Saxon poetry.

Li Po, the author of this poem, lived in China during the time considered to be the golden age of Chinese poetry. His dates are approximately A.D. 701 to 762. Li Po is acclaimed by many as the greatest Chinese poet of all time.

DVONYA, Louis Simpson, p. 52.

Odessa (1): city in southern Russia on the Black Sea.

Chekhov (14): (1860-1904) famous Russian playwright and short-story writer.

WAR POEMS, GROUP FOUR

CAVALRY CROSSING A FORD, Walt Whitman, p. 55.
guidon flags (7): small flags that indicate particular military
units.

VOLUNTARIES, Ralph Waldo Emerson, p. 56.
Voluntaries: volunteer soldiers, as opposed to draftees.
Actually there is more to this poem than the lines printed
in this anthology. The portion printed here is the third
section of the complete poem which was printed in the
Atlantic Monthly in October, 1863. The poem may be re-
garded as a dirge for Colonel Robert Gould Shaw and the
men under his command who were killed in a Civil War
battle.

In July 1863, Colonel Shaw, in the face of half-hostile
public opinion, gave up his commission in a favorite Massachusetts regiment to take command of one of the first enlisted Negro regiments, largely made up of ex-slaves. Shaw,
together with many of his men and officers, were killed on
the slopes of Fort Wagner. A monument depicting Shaw at
the head of his troops stands on the Boston Common.

WAR IS KIND, Stephen Crane, p. 58.
bright splendid shroud (24): flag-covered coffin.

THE ASH AND THE OAK, Louis Simpson, p. 59.
feathered (5): feathered arrows filled the air.
virtue (6): from its Latin derivation the word carries here its
original meaning, *manliness;* hence *courage.*
root (6): the natural curve of a root gave the bow its strength.
billets-doux (11): love letters, suggesting chivalric courtesy.
recoil (18): literally kick-back, but figuratively the idea that
the user inflicts injury upon himself.
Four of the place names in the poem refer to famous battles:
Malplaquet, 1709; *Waterloo,* 1815; *Verdun,* 1916; *Bastogne,*
1944.

Appomattox (13): At Appomattox Court House Robert E. Lee surrendered to Ulysses S. Grant, April 9, 1865.

SUCCESS IS COUNTED SWEETEST,
Emily Dickinson, p. 60.

To comprehend a nectar (3): to understand the sweetness of success.

purple host (5): victorious army.

EIGHTH AIR FORCE, Randall Jarrell, p. 62.

hutment (1): temporary shelter in England for American Air Force bombers.

O Paradiso (4): "Oh paradise on earth . . . ," an aria from Act IV of Meyerbeer's opera *L'Africaine*, sung by the tenor in the role of Vasco da Gama while he is surrounded by his would-be executioners.

man . . . a wolf to man (4-5): reference to Vanzetti's last speech to the Massachusetts court.

Behold the man! (15): the words Pilate used in presenting Christ, wearing the crown of thorns, to the Jews (*John* XIX, 5). The poet's use of this phrase links Christ the saviour with man now trying to save the Christian ethic.

this just man (20): used probably with the intentional ambiguity of "man of justice" and "just a man"—human and not divine.

THE GIFT OUTRIGHT, Robert Frost, p. 63.

Robert Frost recited this poem at the inauguration of President John F. Kennedy on January 20, 1961. (He had first read it as the Phi Beta Kappa poem at William and Mary College, Dec. 5, 1941.)

In Massachusetts, in Virginia (4): the first English colonies.

POEMS OF THE CITY, GROUP FIVE

ACQUAINTED WITH THE NIGHT, Robert Frost, p. 65.

The following passage is to be read with Frost's poem "Acquainted with the Night." It is taken from a talk given by George Bennett to students at Phillips Exeter Academy, where Mr. Bennett taught English for thirty-five years. In his talk Mr. Bennett speaks of the personal significance he found in "Acquainted with the Night."

I know one thing about English, and that is: neither you nor I know what may prove significant for you. I tend, more and more, to think of English as I tend to think of life — as a gigantic puzzle made up of highly complicated pieces. Every once in a while you fit together a few pieces and are elated, for a time. You will never complete the puzzle, but what of that. The only danger is the danger of losing interest in completing it. Just think, ten years from now you will have difficulty in remembering the title of a single book that you read in English 4. Twenty years from now you will have difficulty in remembering the name of your instructor in English 4. Yet, who knows, thirty years from now you may undergo something, experience something, have a sudden sense of understanding that leaves you wordless. As you grope for words, out of your memory, long submerged, may come, say, a line of a poem — a poem that you had forgotten you ever knew, a poem written several hundred years before your time, yet the line seems to define your feeling. Two of the pieces of the puzzle fit, and in delight and wonder you say the line:

I saw eternity the other night

This all sounds pretty vague, doesn't it? Let me risk a personal example, the only kind of example worth giving. A little over a year ago I was in the Massachusetts General Hospital, in a weakened condition. I could not sleep at night. During the day I could doze and even fall asleep. But as soon as the night came, I was wide awake. I spent the day dreading the night. I was irritable; I whined; I speculated wildly, crazily, about myself, my condition.

I remember one night in particular. It was a Sunday night and all night long, hour after hour, I read the Sunday *New York Times*. When I had finished, I reached up and switched off my light. I lay in the dark and waited. It would come soon, I thought, or hoped. And then it came—a sudden flare of light outside my window. Not the sun. An electric light had been turned on outside the building. But I knew what that meant. I knew it meant that, despite the darkness, the first of the day-shift was beginning to arrive. And it seemed to me that from all over the city, doctors, interns, nurses, attendants, maids, janitors were heading toward me, bringing the day. Soon I would hear sounds far below, then footsteps, then voices. And as I lay there relaxed and happy, I said aloud a line of a poem:

I have been one acquainted with the night.

And then, line by line, rhyme by rhyme, I brought back the whole poem until I could say it to myself.

I had read the poem often and knew that it echoed a time when Robert Frost, long before his recognition as a poet, let alone as a great poet, had tramped the streets of London, lonely, attacked by doubt. Now I knew more. This poem about doubt or despair or pain or grief, this poem about the night, was about the dark side of life that we must face—and outface. And that remarkable line

Proclaimed the time was neither wrong nor right

came clearer to me. There was no whining there, no lament about fate, no excuses, no self-deceptions like: "I could have done it if only the time . . .", or like the person the other day, a person angry at satellites and space ships, who said to me bitterly: "There are ten periods in the history of mankind that I would rather have lived in than in the present." Then he listed all ten. And that phrase, "acquainted with"—what a casual offhand way of describing an ordeal. What spirit there was

in that matter-of-fact understatement: "acquainted with."
And as I lay there in the dark looking toward the light,
Robert Frost seemed to reach out toward me with his
fortitude, and the poem seemed to include me with its
courage, its triumph:

I have been acquainted with the night.

GEORGE BENNETT

RIDING THE "A," May Swenson, p. 68.
the "A" train (2): one of the expresses on the New York City
subway system. The poet mentions riding from the West
4th Street station to the 168th Street station. There are
only five stops on this 164-block journey, and the train
moves very rapidly through the tunnel.

CONCRETE TRAP, Elizabeth Coatsworth, p. 70.
Elizabeth Coatsworth made an interesting comment when
she was asked how the poem began. Here is her answer,
from a letter she wrote January 27, 1967:

"Concrete Trap" was written during the Second World
War. For some time we had been reading accounts of
the ruses of Römmel, the German general in North
Africa, which earned him the nickname of "The Desert
Fox." At this time, it was believed that he was hemmed in
by superior forces and every bolt-hole stopped. For some
reason the image of a fox in a maze of unknown city
streets trying to think his way out before the hounds
pulled him down, came to me, and I wrote the poem. Of
course, for once, he didn't get away. But that is history.

RAIN AFTER A VAUDEVILLE SHOW,
Stephen Vincent Benét, p. 71.
harsh light stabbing the eyes (2-3): in the early days of the
movies when a film ended the white screen was flooded
with blinding light from the projectionist's booth.
A fat girl . . . began to sing (4-5): When this poem was

published in 1918, vaudeville acts shared the bill with a movie.

GIVE ME THE SPLENDID SILENT SUN,
Walt Whitman, p. 72.

primal sanities (11): sound and healthy life, close to nature.
war-strife (12): the Civil War.
Ninth-month (22): September.
trottoirs (23): sidewalks.

NIGHT GAME, Rolfe Humphries, p. 74.

William Saroyan (1): American novelist and playwright.
Feldman and *Ott* (16): Both men played for the New York Giants in the 1930s. The setting is the old Polo Grounds in New York City where the Giants played their home games.
underground (32): the subway — perhaps an intended ambiguity.

A SOLITUDE, Denise Levertov, p. 75.

The tale of this subway encounter with a blind man is told with a beautiful directness. If the reader is uncertain how to take the last three lines, with their absence of quotation marks, Denise Levertov's reply to the editor's question about these lines should be of help. In a letter to the editor, written January 4, 1967, she explained that the blind man does not speak the words *I am* aloud. She went on to say:

. . . he does not speak aloud, but everything about him is an utterance of the essence of existence, the being, the consciousness of every individual. It also, as I came to realize after writing it, connects with the "*I am*" of God and perhaps one can consider that essence as a spark of the Divine in each individual as the Hassidim and other mystics have thought of it. . . . The *nowhere* [in the next to last line] I think is nowhere because, lacking sight, by which I and most of us live perhaps more than by any other of the senses, every place is the same to him.

SAL'S ATOMIC SUBMARINES, L. E. Sissman, p. 77.
This poem was first published in *The New Yorker* magazine in a group of eight poems under the heading "The West Forties: Morning, Noon and Night."
Jesus (1): The Spanish pronunciation of this name is *Hay-soos´*.
indigenes (13): natives.

THE GOOD WILDERNESS, GROUP SIX

THE WAKING, Theodore Roethke, p. 79.
This poem re-creates one of Roethke's early boyhood experiences. While an undergraduate at Michigan, Roethke wrote of himself: "I can sense the moods of nature almost instinctively. Ever since I could walk, I have spent as much time as I could in the open."

THE GREAT SCARF OF BIRDS, John Updike, p. 80.
Cape Ann (1): on the northeast coast of Massachusetts.
Lot's wife (29): fleeing with her husband from the doomed city of Sodom, she looked back and was turned to a pillar of salt *(Genesis XIX)*.

THE RHODORA, Ralph Waldo Emerson, p. 82.
Then Beauty is its own excuse for being (12): In his essay "Nature" Emerson wrote: "This element Beauty I call an ultimate end. No reason can be asked or given why the soul seeks beauty. Beauty, in its largest and profoundest sense, is one expression for the universe."

NEW HAMPSHIRE, Donald Hall, p. 83.
the EAT signs (7): signs once on the roofs of diners now are amidst the debris on cellar floors.
This poem and Thoreau's "What's the railroad to me?" both express pleasure in the apparent disregard nature has for the works of man.

EEL-GRASS, Edna St. Vincent Millay, p. 85.

Eel-grass: This marine plant with its long narrow leaves usually grows in inlets of the sea. In 1933 the poet and her husband bought Ragged Island, off Harpswell, Maine, and spent the next seventeen summers there, living in great simplicity and with no regular communication with the mainland.

WHAT'S THE RAILROAD TO ME?

Henry David Thoreau, p. 86.

The railroad was first built through Concord during Thoreau's lifetime. He loved the undisturbed wilderness and feared he was seeing it come to an end. Thoreau was an early conservationist who urged establishing national parks.

THE FLOWER-FED BUFFALOES, Vachel Lindsay, p. 86.

Blackfeet . . . Pawnees (13-14): American Indians of the plains states.

This poem is a nostalgic elegy for the Wild West of yesteryear.

ABOVE PATE VALLEY, Gary Snyder, p. 88.

Pate Valley: in the high country north of Yosemite Valley in the Sierra Nevada, California.

Aspen (9): a type of tree, whose leaves flutter in the least breeze. These flutterings are the source of the trembling shadows mentioned in line 13.

obsidian (15): the name of the black volcanic glass.

single-jack (26): short-handled hammer used in mining.

MORE FIGURATIVELY, GROUP SEVEN

IN A STATION OF THE METRO, Ezra Pound, p. 91.

the Metro: the name given to the subway system in Paris.

HOKKU, Richard Wright, p. 91.

hokku (often spelled haiku): a Japanese verse form consisting of three lines with a total of seventeen syllables, usually on some subject in nature.

BIRCHES, Robert Frost, p. 92.
dragged to the withered bracken by the load (14): bent down among the withered ferns by the weight of ice.

BIG WIND, Theodore Roethke, p. 95.
The setting is Roethke's father's greenhouses in Saginaw, Michigan, where the poet spent his boyhood.

CAT ON A COUCH, Barbara Howes, p. 97.
leafy tricorned ears (8): leaf-shaped ears, with three corners.

TELEPHONE POLES, John Updike, p. 98.
a Gorgon's head (11): the Gorgons, in Greek myth, were three sisters with snaky hair, who turned all beholders to stone.
stun us to stone (12): electrocute us.
twitter (20): here used as a noun.

VOYAGES I, Hart Crane, p. 100.
striped urchins (2): small boys wearing striped jerseys.
treble interjections (6): shrill, high-pitched shouts.
spry cordage of your bodies (14): quick-moving, thin and sinewy bodies.
caresses too lichen-faithful (14-15): a lichen is a type of plant composed of an alga and a fungus which live together in a mutually close, dependent relationship. Caresses that are too "lichen-faithful" are therefore, probably, too close or intense — dangerously so.

THE MARSH, W. D. Snodgrass, p. 102.
spatterdock (1): a large plant which grows in ditches and marshes and sends up a single stalk with a large floppy leaf. Children sometimes call it "elephant ears."
Stick in the mud, old heart (17): the speaker recognizes himself in this dead and soggy place he is walking about in. The scene becomes for him an image of his own life.

THE HERON, Raymond Holden, p. 103.
winnow (3): to separate, as a farmer does chaff from grain.

LIMITED, Carl Sandburg, p. 104.
limited: a word sometimes used to refer to a fast train that stops at only a few stations. In its other meanings, *limited*, of course, also suggests something narrow-minded or unspeculative.

FARTHER OUT, GROUP EIGHT

THE ROPEWALK, Henry Wadsworth Longfellow, p. 107.
hulk (3): the remains of a dismantled ship.
mountebanks (25): unscrupulous pretenders.
Fowlers (53): bird hunters and trappers.
snares (53): nooses for catching birds or other small game.
angler (54): fisherman.
line and lead (59): a weight attached to a rope, tossed over a ship's side to measure the water's depth.

LITTLE ELEGY, X. J. Kennedy, p. 109.
elegy: a lament for the dead or a thoughtful, melancholy poem.
trip up death (8): keep death from being frightening or in any way terrible.

SALEM, Robert Lowell, p. 110.
spindrift (1): sea spray.
Morpheus (4): god of dreams.
Charon (7): In Greek mythology, the boatman who ferried dead souls to Hades.
Great Banks (11): fishing grounds southeast of Newfoundland.
quartered the Leviathan's flanks (13): cut up the great whales harpooned at sea.
fought the British Lion to his knees (14): American naval victories in the War of 1812.

ORIENT WHEAT, Adrienne Rich, p. 111.

Puzzled by the title, the editor of this anthology wrote to Adrienne Rich who explained the meaning of "Orient Wheat" as follows:

> The title is from Traherne's *Third Century of Meditations*, *#3*, . . . the passage beginning "The Corn was Orient and Immortal Wheat, which never had been reaped, nor was ever sown . . ." which describes the radiance of the young child's vision of the world, later "corrupted and made to learn the Dirty Devices of this World." The poem is of course a reflection on the truism that one's own good young days seem always to have been the golden age.　*Letter from Adrienne Rich, January 1, 1967.*

CLIFF KLINGENHAGEN,
　　　　　　　　Edwin Arlington Robinson, p. 114.
wormwood (5): a bitter drink.

BOATS IN A FOG, Robinson Jeffers, p. 115.

The scorn which Jeffers expresses here for "sports and gallantries, the stage, the arts, the antics of dancers, the exuberant voices of music" is typical of the attitude expressed in much of his poetry. This attitude is somewhat Puritanical. For Jeffers the greatest beauty is to be found in the "bitter earnestness" of creatures struggling to eke out a living from indifferent or hostile nature. In this attitude he is similar to many eighteenth century American writers.

DAYS, Ralph Waldo Emerson, p. 116.
　hypocritic (1): pretending to be something that they are not.
　dervishes (2): members of a Moslem religious order who take vows of poverty and chastity and are noted for the exercises they do—whirling, howling, etc.
　diadems (4): crowns.
　fagots (4): bundles of sticks used for fuel.

pleached (7): fenced or covered over by interlaced branches.
fillet (11): headband.

JUGGLER, Richard Wilbur, p. 117.

Richard Wilbur responded to the editor's queries about this poem as follows:

> I'd say that *gravity* (line 7) refers to the force which juggling defies, and to the creeping dullness which—unless we combat it—destroys our power to see the earth freshly and delight in it. The juggler undoubtedly suggests various things, but I have in mind particularly the artist, and I mean there to be a contrast between the kind of art which contrives a private paradise *(a small heaven about his ears)* and that which restores delight to the earthly and everyday.

BRAHMA, Ralph Waldo Emerson, p. 118.

Brahma: In Hindu religious thought Brahma is the ultimate God of all being: the Creator. He is the supreme and eternal essence or spirit of the universe. Brahma is the speaker in this poem. Emerson was keenly interested in Oriental philosophy and religion and from it drew the idea of a God who participates in every aspect of creation, both human and natural.

the red slayer (1): death or a murderer.

Brahmin (12): Hindu of the highest caste, usually a priest.

THE GODDESS, Denise Levertov, p. 119.

lip service (1): allegiance by words.

Lie Castle (4): capitalized to signal the use of allegory, and perhaps remind the reader of Christian's dangerous encounters in Bunyan's *Pilgrim's Progress*.

Denise Levertov has written that this poem "recalls one of those confrontations with Truth that every person, every soul, must sometimes experience if he or she is to live, to grow; and especially one who is a poet—for poets have a genius for lying and an adoration for the truth, and it may be that the driving impulse of every poet is to maintain the dynamic interplay of these two passions."

THE SHEAVES, Edwin Arlington Robinson, p. 121.
Sheaves: bundles of wheat, cut and tied, and still in the harvest field.
undivined (3): undiscovered.

ELDORADO, Edgar Allan Poe, p. 122.
Eldorado: In Spanish it is two words, *El Dorado*, meaning a place of tremendous wealth and abundance; utopia.
bedight (1): dressed, costumed.
Valley of the Shadow (21): the shadow of death.

NOTES ON THE POETS' LIVES

STEPHEN VINCENT BENÉT (1898-1943): born in Bethlehem, Pennsylvania. A graduate of Yale. Both a poet (*John Brown's Body, Ballads and Poems*) and a writer of stories ("The Devil and Daniel Webster" and "Thirteen O'Clock"). Awarded Pulitzer Prize for poetry for 1929.

PHILIP BOOTH: born in New Hampshire, 1925. Educated at Dartmouth. Served as pilot in the Army Air Force in World War II. His poems are published in *Letter from a Distant Land*. Has taught at Bowdoin, Dartmouth, Wellesley, and Syracuse.

GWENDOLYN BROOKS: born in Topeka, Kansas, 1917. Has lived most of her life in Chicago. Books of her poems include *Annie Allen* (awarded the Pulitzer Prize for 1949), *A Street in Bronzeville*, and *The Bean Eaters*. Besides poetry, has written fiction and verse for children.

ELIZABETH COATSWORTH: born in Buffalo, New York, 1893. A graduate of Vassar and Columbia. Traveled in the Orient. Author of over thirty books, including five collections of poems (*Fox Footprints, Compass Rose, Country Poems*), and many stories for children. Awarded the Newbery Medal for *The Cat Who Went to Heaven*, 1930.

HART CRANE (1899-1932): born in Garrettsville, Ohio. Published only two books of poems, *White Buildings* (1926) and *The Bridge* (1932), but was a notable and influential poet. Moved from a poetry of despair toward mystical affirmation, reflecting the influence of Walt Whitman's faith in America's democratic future.

STEPHEN CRANE (1871-1900): born in Newark, New Jersey. Both a great prose writer (*The Red Badge of Courage*, "The Open Boat," "The Bride Comes to Yellow Sky") and poet ("The Black Riders" and "War Is Kind"). His poetry, written mostly in free verse, gains its power from dramatic, often grotesque encounters, understatement, and irony.

E. E. CUMMINGS (1894-1962): born in Cambridge, Massachusetts. Majored in classical languages at Harvard. Drove ambulance in World War I; war prisoner (*The Enormous Room*). In his poetry (*Poems 1923-1954*) explored new type-spacing of the text, often omitted capital letters and punctuation.

EMILY DICKINSON (1830-1886): born in Amherst, Massachusetts. Educated at Mt. Holyoke. Lived a life of virtual retirement in Amherst. Began writing poetry in 1861. All six volumes of her poems were published after her death; they have established her place among the great American poets.

RALPH WALDO EMERSON (1803-1882): born in Boston. Educated at Harvard; clergyman; philosophical essayist ("Nature," "Self-Reliance," "Compensation," etc.); and poet. Lecturer, champion of freedom and individualism, long a resident of Concord, Mass., and the friend of Thoreau, Hawthorne, and Carlyle.

KENNETH FEARING (1902-1961): born in Chicago. Besides five books of poetry (*Afternoon of a Pawnbroker and Other Poems* and *New and Selected Poems*) wrote several novels. His poetry, influenced possibly by Sandburg's social realism and urban themes, treats modern life with Fearing's own brand of satire and humor.

ROBERT FITZGERALD: born in Geneva, New York, 1910. Studied philosophy and classical languages at Harvard and Trinity College, Cambridge. Besides his own poetry, he is noted for his translations of Sophocles and Homer. In 1965 he was appointed Boylston Professor of Rhetoric and Oratory at Harvard.

ROBERT FRANCIS: born in Upland, Pennsylvania, 1901. Educated at Harvard. Has lived many years at Fort Juniper, Amherst, Mass. Phi Beta Kappa poet at Harvard, 1960. His sixth book, *Come Out Into the Sun, Poems New and Selected* (1965), collects the work of three decades.

ROBERT FROST (1874-1963): born in San Francisco. Attended Dartmouth for several months; later had two years at Harvard. Was forty before his first book of poems, *A Boy's Will*, was published—in England. Became the dominant American poet of the mid-twentieth century. Awarded the Pulitzer Prize for poetry four times. *Complete Poems* (1949); *In the Clearing* (1962).

DONALD HALL: born in New Haven, Connecticut, 1928. Attended Harvard and Oxford. Three books of his poems, *Exiles and Marriages*, *The Dark Houses*, and *A Roof of Tiger Lilies*, and two volumes of prose, *String Too Short to Be*

Saved and *Henry Moore*, have been published. Teaches at the University of Michigan.

RAYMOND HOLDEN: born in New York City, 1894. A graduate of Princeton. Poet, editor, and naturalist. His books of poems include: *Granite and Alabaster* (1922), *Natural History* (1938), *The Arrow at the Heel* (1940), *Selected Poems* (1946), and *The Reminding Salt* (1964).

BARBARA HOWES: born in Boston, 1914. A graduate of Bennington College. Founder and editor of the literary quarterly *Chimera*. Has published two collections of poems: *Light and Dark* (1959) and *Looking Up at Leaves* (1966).

ROLFE HUMPHRIES: born in Philadelphia, 1894. (His father was a Phi Beta Kappa graduate of Cornell and a major league catcher.) Humphries is a graduate of Amherst. Author of seven books of poems; translator of Virgil and Ovid; anthologist of American poetry; teacher of the classics, later of creative writing, at Amherst (1958-66).

RANDALL JARRELL (1914-1965): born in Nashville, Tennessee. A graduate of Vanderbilt University. Poet, novelist, and critic. Taught at Sarah Lawrence, Kenyon, and the University of North Carolina. Served for three and a half years in the Army Air Force in World War II. Received the National Book Award for poetry in 1961.

ROBINSON JEFFERS (1887-1962): born in Pittsburgh. Attended Occidental College. Lived for a half century in semi-isolation at Carmel, California. Wrote *Tamar* (1924), *Roan Stallion* (1925), *Selected Poems* (1938), *Be Angry at the Sun* (1941), *The Double Axe* (1948), *Hungerfield* (1954).

X. J. KENNEDY: born in Dover, New Jersey, 1929. Served with the Navy in the Atlantic fleet; attended the Sorbonne. Formerly poetry editor, *The Paris Review*. Has taught at Michigan, North Carolina, Tufts, and the University of California. His poems have been collected in *Nude Descending a Staircase* (1961).

GALWAY KINNELL: born in Pawtucket, Rhode Island, 1927. Educated at Princeton and Rochester. Taught at universities in Chicago, Grenoble, France, and Teheran, Iran. His poems are collected in *What a Kingdom It Was* (1960).

KENNETH KOCH: born in Cincinnati, Ohio, 1925. A.B. from Harvard College; M.A. and Ph.D. from Columbia University. Lives in New York City and teaches at Columbia University. Writes poetry and plays. Published works include *Poems* (1953), *Thank You and Other Poems* (1962), *Bertha and Other Plays* (1966).

DENISE LEVERTOV: born in Essex, England, 1923. A nurse during World War II, she married an American and has lived in the U.S.A. since 1948. Has published seven books of poems: *The Double Image, Here and Now, Overland to the Islands, With Eyes at the Back of Our Heads, The Jacob's Ladder, O Taste and See*, and *The Sorrow Dance*.

VACHEL LINDSAY (1879-1931): born in Springfield, Illinois. Attended Hiram College. In the old troubadour tradition traveled the countryside, preaching a gospel of beauty and paying his way with a pamphlet entitled *Rhymes to be Traded for Bread*. In 1914, publication of *The Congo and Other Poems* brought instant fame.

HENRY WADSWORTH LONGFELLOW (1807-1882): born in Portland, Maine. A graduate of Bowdoin College. Author of *Song of Hiawatha, The Courtship of Miles Standish, Tales of a Wayside Inn, Evangeline: A Tale of Acadie*. Taught modern languages at Bowdoin and Harvard.

AMY LOWELL (1874-1925): born in Brookline, Massachusetts. An early member of the Imagist movement in poetry (c.1912-1924); experimenter and innovator with free verse. Author of eight books of poems, critical studies of American and French poets, and a two-volume biography of John Keats.

ROBERT LOWELL: born in Boston, 1917. A graduate of Kenyon College. Author of six books of poems, including *Lord Weary's Castle* (1946) and *For the Union Dead* (1964). The recipient of many honors, including the National Book Award and the Pulitzer Prize for poetry.

EDGAR LEE MASTERS (1869-1950): born in Kansas, but spent boyhood in New Salem, Illinois, where young Abraham Lincoln tended store and studied law. Attended Knox College, then practiced law successfully in Chicago. Wrote more than a dozen books; however, his lasting fame rests on one, *Spoon River Anthology* (1915).

PHYLLIS McGINLEY: born in Ontario, Oregon, 1905. Perhaps best known for light, satirical verse in *The New Yorker*. She has been honored for all her work, winning the Pulitzer Prize for poetry in 1960 for *Times Three: Selected Verse*.

JOSEPHINE MILES: born in Chicago, 1911. Poet, critic, and teacher. On the English faculty of the University of California at Berkeley. For *Poems: 1930-1960* she received a Shelley Memorial Award.

EDNA ST. VINCENT MILLAY (1892-1950): born in Rockland, Maine. Attended Vassar College, then lived in Greenwich Village. Spent her latter years on a farm in New York State. Among the collections of her lyrics and sonnets: *Renascence; A Few Figs from Thistles; The Harp Weaver.* Awarded Pulitzer Prize in 1923.

MARIANNE MOORE: born in St. Louis, 1887. A graduate of Bryn Mawr. Editor of *The Dial*, 1925-29. Translator of *The Fables of La Fontaine.* For her *Collected Poems* (1951) she was awarded the Pulitzer Prize, the National Book Award, and the Bollingen Award. Wrote *O to Be a Dragon* (1959) and *Tell Me, Tell Me,* (1966).

JOHN R. NASH: born in Royalton, Vermont, 1938. A graduate of Dartmouth and Stanford. Poems in *The Atlantic*

Monthly, 1961, 1962. Author of *Our Devil Takes a Holiday* (Lunenburg, Vt.: Stinehour Press, 1963).

HOWARD NEMEROV: born in New York City, 1920. A graduate of Harvard. Aviator with the Royal Canadian Air Force. Author of novels, works of criticism, and seven books of poems, including *The Image and the Law*, *Guide to the Ruins*, *The Salt Garden*, and *The Next Room of the Dream*. Has taught at Bennington; is now at Brandeis University.

EDGAR ALLAN POE (1809-1849): born in Boston. Attended University of Virginia and West Point. Both poet ("Tamerlane," "The Raven," "Annabel Lee," "Ulalume," "Eldorado," "The Bells") and author of literary criticism and short stories ("The Gold Bug," "The Fall of the House of Usher," "Murders in the Rue Morgue," "The Black Cat").

EZRA POUND: born in Hailey, Idaho, 1885. After college and teaching at Hamilton and Pennsylvania, Pound lived abroad, first in London and Paris, finally at Rapallo, Italy. Wrote *Cathay* (1915), *Umbra* (1920), *Cantos* (1925-48). Charged with treason in 1945 and committed to St. Elizabeth's Hospital, Washington; released in 1958 and allowed to return to Italy.

ADRIENNE RICH: born in Baltimore, 1929. A graduate of Radcliffe College. Her books of poems include *A Change of World*, *The Diamond Cutters*, *Snapshots of a Daughter-in-Law*, and *Necessities of Life*. A Guggenheim Fellow and holder of an Amy Lowell Traveling Scholarship. Phi Beta Kappa poet at Harvard, 1966.

EDWIN ARLINGTON ROBINSON (1869-1935): born in Head Tide, Maine. Attended Harvard College; later lived in New York City, summering at the MacDowell Colony, Peterboro, N.H. A major American poet; wrote thirteen books of poetry (*Captain Craig*, *The Town Down the River*, etc.); thrice awarded the Pulitzer Prize for poetry.

THEODORE ROETHKE (1908-1963): born in Saginaw, Michigan. Attended Michigan State University and Harvard. Taught at several Eastern colleges before becoming professor of English at the University of Washington, Seattle. Awarded the Pulitzer Prize for poetry in 1954. Wrote *The Waking, Poems 1933-1953* and *Words for the Wind* (1957).

CARL SANDBURG (1878-1967): born in Galesburg, Illinois. Worked as a porter, truck handler, dishwasher, harvest hand, finally a journalist. Won immediate fame as a poet, writing in free verse, with *Chicago Poems* (1916), *Cornhuskers* (1918), *Smoke and Steel* (1920), *Slabs of the Sunburnt West* (1922). Author of a monumental biography of Abraham Lincoln.

ALAN SEEGER (1888-1916): born in New York City. A graduate of Harvard; living in France at the outbreak of World War I, he enlisted in the Foreign Legion. Killed in action at Belloy-en-Santerre (July 4, 1916).

LOUIS SIMPSON: born in Jamaica, W.I., 1923. Came to America in 1940; attended Columbia. Served three years in the U.S. Army; received American citizenship at Berchtesgaden. Teaches at the University of California, Berkeley. Author of *The Arrivistes, Good News of Death, A Dream of Governors*, and *Selected Poems*. Awarded the Pulitzer Prize for poetry, 1964.

L. E. SISSMAN: born in Detroit, Michigan, 1928. Attended Harvard, where he won the Garrison Poetry Prize. Vice-president and creative director of Kenyon & Eckhardt Advertising, Boston. His poems have largely appeared in *The New Yorker* and *The Atlantic Monthly;* in preparation is a collection of his poems entitled *Dying: An Introduction*.

W. D. SNODGRASS: born in Wilkinsburg, Pennsylvania, 1926. Attended Geneva College and the University of Iowa. Teaches at Wayne State University, Detroit. Awarded the

Pulitzer Prize for poetry in 1959 for a collection entitled *Heart's Needle*.

GARY SNYDER: born in San Francisco, 1930. Attended Reed College, majoring in cultural anthropology. Did graduate study at Indiana University and the University of California at Berkeley, where he now teaches. His books of poems are *Riprap* (1959) and *Myths and Texts* (1960).

THEODORE SPENCER (1902-1949): born in Villanova, Pennsylvania. Attended Princeton and Cambridge University, England. Boylston Professor of Rhetoric and Oratory, Harvard; Shakespearean critic (*Death and Elizabethan Tragedy*); and poet (*The Paradox in the Circle*, 1941, and *An Act of Life*, 1944).

WILLIAM STAFFORD: born in Hutchinson, Kansas, 1914. Educated at the universities of Kansas, Wisconsin, and Iowa. Collections of his poems include: *West of Your City*, (1960); *Travelling through the Dark*, National Book Award for poetry (1962); and *The Rescued Year*, (1966). Teaches at Lewis and Clark College in Portland, Oregon.

WALLACE STEVENS (1879-1955): born in Reading, Pennsylvania. Educated at Harvard and New York Law School. Practiced law, and from 1916 until his death was an insurance executive in Hartford, Conn. His first book of poems, *Harmonium*, was published in 1919. His *Collected Poems* was published in 1954.

MAY SWENSON: born in Logan, Utah, 1919. Graduate of Utah State University; newspaper reporter in Utah; editor with New Directions in New York City. Received Guggenheim and National Institute of Arts awards in 1959-60. Her fifth book of poems, *Half Sun Half Sleep*, published in 1967; earlier volumes are *A Cage of Spines* and *To Mix with Time*.

HENRY DAVID THOREAU (1817-62): born in Concord, Massachusetts. A graduate of Harvard. Naturalist, surveyor, hermit, journalist, and poet. His journals fill twenty volumes, but his secure place in American literature is based on the two books published in his lifetime: *Walden or Life in the Woods*, and *A Week on the Concord and Merrimack Rivers*.

JOHN UPDIKE: born in 1932. Attended schools in Shillington, Pennsylvania, and Harvard College. Studied art in England. On the staff of *The New Yorker*. The author of novels *(The Poorhouse Fair; Rabbit, Run;* etc.) and two books of poetry *(The Carpentered Hen* and *Telephone Poles)*. Lives on Cape Ann in Ipswich, Mass.

WALT WHITMAN (1819-1892): born on Long Island, New York. Journalist, later editor of the *Brooklyn Daily Eagle*. Served as a hospital nurse during the Civil War. In 1855 published the first edition of *Leaves of Grass*, which he revised and enlarged in many subsequent editions. Lived the last twenty years of his life in Camden, N. J.

RICHARD WILBUR: born in New York City, 1921. Attended Amherst College. Served in U. S. Army in Italy and France. A Junior Fellow at Harvard College, 1947-50. Author of *Things of This World* (1956), *Poems, 1943-56, Advice to a Prophet* (1961). Awarded both National Book Award and Pulitzer Prize. Has taught at Harvard, Wellesley, and Wesleyan.

WILLIAM CARLOS WILLIAMS (1883-1963): born in Rutherford, New Jersey. Led parallel lives as a physician and a poet; wrote his first poems in medical school. During fifty years, he delivered two thousand babies in his native town and published over forty volumes of poetry, short stories, novels, and an autobiography.

RICHARD WRIGHT (1908-1960): born near Natchez, Mississippi. Virtually self-educated. Porter, messenger, ditchdigger, clerk in Memphis, Tenn.; later in Chicago. Died in France. Author of *Uncle Tom's Children* (1938), *Native Son* (1940), *Twelve Million Black Voices* (1941), and *Black Boy* (1945).

ABOUT THE EDITOR

PAUL MOLLOY: taught English for twenty-four years at Phillips Exeter Academy, Exeter, New Hampshire. Before teaching at Exeter, he taught at Harvard University and at the Hanover, Massachusetts, high school. Mr. Molloy is co-editor of *Cavalcade of Poems*, published by Scholastic.

Index of Poems and Poets